CONTENTS

Parent and Child

Parent and Child

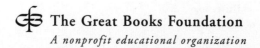

The Great Books Foundation

A nonprofit educational organization

First Printing
9 8 7 6 5 4 3 2 1 0

Published and distributed by

 The Great Books Foundation
A nonprofit educational organization

35 East Wacker Drive, Suite 2300
Chicago, IL 60601-2298

"So that's why Kafka views his writing as a 'long and drawn-out leave-taking' from his father!" "Is Agamemnon powerless to save his daughter Iphigeneia?" "Do parents control whether their children live joyfully or sorowfully?"

Anyone who has been in a book discussion group has experienced the joy of new insight. Sometimes an idea or question occurs to us during the group meeting. Often, it is afterward—sometimes much later—that an idea we had overlooked unexpectedly strikes us with new force. A good group becomes a community of minds. We share perspectives, questions, insights, and surprises. Our fellow readers challenge and broaden our thinking as we probe deeply into characters and ideas. They help us resolve questions, and raise new ones, in a creative process that connects literature with life.

It is this kind of experience that makes book discussion groups worthwhile, and that the Great Books Foundation fosters for thousands of readers around the world.

The Great Books Foundation is a pioneer of book discussion groups that bring together dedicated readers who wish to continue to learn throughout their lives. The literature anthologies published by the Foundation have been the focus of many enlightening discussions among people of all educational backgrounds and walks of life. And the *shared inquiry* method practiced by Great Books groups has proven to be a powerful approach to literature that solves many practical concerns of new discussion groups: How can we maintain a flow of ideas? What kinds of questions should we discuss? How can we keep the discussion focused on the reading so that we use our time together to really get at the heart of a work—to learn from it and each other?

With the publication of its 50th Anniversary Series, the Great Books Foundation continues and expands upon its tradition of helping all readers engage in a meaningful exchange of ideas about outstanding works of literature.

ABOUT PARENT AND CHILD

The reading selections in *Parent and Child* have been chosen to stimulate lively shared inquiry discussions. This collection brings together works from around the world that speak to each other on a theme of universal human significance. In this volume you will find a classic Greek drama by Euripides; powerful short fiction by William Faulkner; modern works by the Israeli author A. B. Yehoshua, the African American author Andrea Lee, and the Caribbean author Jamaica Kincaid; and a psychologically revealing letter from Franz Kafka to his father. In addition to the prose selections, you will discuss poems by W. B. Yeats and Randall Jarrell alongside contemporary works by Sharon Olds and the Nobel Prize-winning West Indian poet Derek Walcott.

These are carefully crafted works that readers will interpret in different ways. They portray characters whose lives and motivations are complex, embody concepts that go beyond simple analysis, and raise many questions to inspire extended reflection.

As an aid to reading and discussion, open-ended *interpretive questions* are included with each selection in the volume, and also for the recommended novels *Persuasion* by Jane Austen and *Billiards at Half-past Nine* by Heinrich Böll. A fundamental or *basic* interpretive question about the meaning of the selection is printed in boldface, followed by a list of related questions that will help you fully discuss the issue raised by the basic question. Passages for *textual analysis* that you may want to look at closely during discussion are suggested for each set of questions. Questions under the heading "For Further Reflection" can be used at the end of discussion to help your group consider the reading selection in a broader context.

About Shared Inquiry

The success of Great Books discussions depends not only on thought-provoking literature, but also on the *shared inquiry* method of discussion. A shared inquiry discussion begins with a basic interpretive question—a genuine question about the meaning of the selection that continues to be puzzling even after careful reading. As participants offer different possible answers to this question, the discussion leader or members of the group follow up on the ideas that are voiced, asking questions about how responses relate to the original question or to new ideas, and probing what specifically in the text prompted the response.

In shared inquiry discussion, readers think for themselves about the selection, and do not rely on critical or biographical sources outside the text for ideas about its meaning. Discussion remains focused on the text. Evidence for opinions is found in the selection. Because interpretive questions have no single "correct answer," participants are encouraged to entertain a range of ideas. The exchange of ideas is open and spontaneous, a common search for understanding that leads to closer, more illuminating reading.

Shared inquiry fosters a habit of critical questioning and thinking. It encourages patience in the face of complexity, and a respect for the opinions of others. As participants explore the work in depth, they try out ideas, reconsider simple answers, and synthesize interpretations. Over time, shared inquiry engenders a profound experience of intellectual intimacy as your group searches together for meaning in literature.

IMPROVING YOUR DISCUSSIONS

The selections in *Parent and Child* will support six meetings of your discussion group (we recommend that you plan to discuss the short selections "Barn Burning" and "New African" at the same session). Discussions usually last about two hours, and are guided by a member of the group who acts as leader. Since the leader has no special knowledge or qualification beyond a genuine curiosity about the text, any member of the group may lead discussion. The leader carefully prepares the interpretive questions that he or she wants to explore with the group, and is primarily responsible for continuing the process of questioning that maintains the flow of ideas.

To ensure a successful discussion, we encourage you to make it a policy to read the selection twice. A first reading will familiarize you with the plot and ideas of a selection; on a second reading you will read more reflectively and discover many aspects of the work that deepen your thinking about it. Allowing a few days to pass between your readings will also help you approach a second reading with deeper insight.

Read the selection actively. Make marginal comments that you might want to refer to in discussion. While our interpretive questions can help you think about different aspects of the work, jotting down your own questions as you read is the best way to engage with the selection and bring a wealth of ideas and meaningful questions to discussion.

During discussion, expect a variety of answers to the basic question. Follow up carefully on these different ideas. Refer to and read from the text often—by way of explaining your answer, and to see if the rest of the group understands the author's words the same way you do. (You will often be surprised!) As your group looks closely at the text, many new ideas will arise.

While leaders in shared inquiry discussion strive to keep comments focused on the text and on the basic interpretive question the group is discussing, the entire group can share responsibility for politely refocusing comments that wander from the text into personal anecdotes or issues that begin to sidetrack discussion.

Remember that during shared inquiry discussion you are investigating differing perspectives on the reading, not social issues. Talk should be about characters in the story, not about participants' own lives. By maintaining this focus, each discussion will be new and interesting, with each participant bringing a different perspective to bear on the text. After the work has been explored thoroughly on its own terms, your thinking about important issues of the day or in your own life will be enhanced. We have found that it is best to formally set aside a time—perhaps the last half-hour of discussion, or perhaps over coffee afterward—for members of the group to share personal experiences and opinions that go beyond a discussion of the selection.

DISCUSSING THE POETRY SELECTIONS

Many book groups shy away from the challenge of discussing poetry, but the shared inquiry method will enable you to make poetry a very satisfying part of your discussion group. Poetry, by its very nature, communicates ideas through suggestion, allusion, and resonance. Because meaning in poetry resides in the interaction between author and reader, and is brought to light through the pooling of different perspectives and readers' responses, poems are ideal for shared inquiry discussion.

We suggest that you discuss the five poems in *Parent and Child* in turn, rather than all together as a group. The accompanying interpretive questions will help you focus on each poem individually, and the questions marked "For Further Reflection" will help you consider common and differing elements of the poems.

It is helpful to read each poem aloud before beginning discussion. Because poetry is usually more densely constructed than prose and highly selective in detail, it often lends itself to what we call *textual analysis*—looking closely at particular lines, words, and images as an entryway to discussing the whole work. Having readers share their different associations with a word or image can often help broaden interpretations.

DISCUSSING THE NOVELS

Of course, many novels come to mind that relate to the theme of parent and child. We have recommended *Persuasion* and *Billiards at Half-past Nine* as particularly enriching novels on this theme, and have provided interpretive questions that can be a significant aid to the reader. Even readers familiar with these novels will find a shared inquiry discussion of them a new and rewarding experience.

Most shared inquiry groups discuss a novel at a single discussion; some prefer to spread the discussion over more than one session, especially for longer novels. Since it is usually not realistic to expect participants to read a novel twice in full before discussion, we recommend that you at least reread parts of the novel that seemed especially important to you or that raised a number of questions in your mind. Our passages for textual analysis suggest parts of the novel where reading twice might be most valuable. You might even begin your discussion, after posing a basic question, by looking closely at one or two short passages to get people talking about central ideas and offering a variety of opinions that can be probed and expanded into a discussion of the whole work.

HOW THE GREAT BOOKS FOUNDATION CAN HELP YOU

The Great Books Foundation can be a significant resource for you and your discussion group. Our staff conducts shared inquiry workshops throughout the country that will help you or your entire group conduct better discussions. Thousands of people—from elementary school teachers and college professors to those who just love books and ideas—have found our workshops to be an enjoyable experience that changes forever how they approach literature.

The Foundation publishes a variety of reading series that might interest you. We invite you to call us at 1-800-222-5870 or visit our Web site at http://www.greatbooks.org. We can help you start a book group, put you in touch with established Great Books groups in your area, or give you information about many special events—such as poetry weekends or week-long discussion institutes—sponsored by Great Books groups around the country.

Finally, we invite you to inquire about Junior Great Books for students in kindergarten through high school, to learn how you can help develop the next generation of book lovers and shared inquiry participants.

We hope you enjoy *Parent and Child* and that it inaugurates many years of exciting discussions for your group. Great Books programs—for children as well as adults—are founded on the idea that readers discussing together can achieve insight and great pleasure from literature. We look forward, with you, to cultivating this idea through the next century.

*Footnotes by the author are not bracketed; footnotes by
the Great Books Foundation, an editor,
or a translator are [bracketed].*

THE CONTINUING
SILENCE OF A POET

A. B. Yehoshua

A. B. YEHOSHUA (1936–   ) was born
in Jerusalem and lives in Haifa, where he
teaches comparative literature at Haifa
University. His novels include *A Late
Divorce, Mr. Mani,* and *Open Heart.*
Active in the Israeli peace movement,
Yehoshua has also published a collection
of essays on Zionism titled *Between
Right and Right.*

H E WAS LATE again last night, and when he did
come in he made no effort to enter quietly. As though my own
sleep did not matter. His steps echoed through the empty house
for a long time. He kept the lights in the hall on and fussed
about endlessly with papers. At last he fell silent. I groped my
way back towards the light, vague sleep of old age. And then,
the rain. For three weeks now this persistent rain, sheets of
water grinding down the panes.

Where does he go at night? I do not know. I once managed
to follow him through several streets, but an old acquaintance,
an incorrigible prose writer, buttonholed me at a street corner
and meanwhile the boy disappeared.

The rains are turning this plain into a morass of asphalt,
sand, and water. Tel Aviv in winter—town without drainage, no
outlets, spawning lakes. And the sea beyond, murky and
unclean, rumbling as though in retreat from the sprawling
town, sea become background.

Not five yet but the windows are turning gray. What was it? He appeared in my dream, stood there in full view before me, not far from the seashore, I think, dark birds were in his lap, and he quelled their fluttering. His smile amazed me. He stood and faced me, looked hard at me, and gave a feeble smile.

Now the faint sound of snoring reaches me from his room and I know I shall sleep no more. Another boat sails tomorrow or the day after and I expect I shall board it at last. This anguish will dissolve, I know. I have only to preserve my dignity till the moment of parting. Another twenty hours or so, only.

Though I do not see him now, I know he is asleep, hands over heart, eyes shut, mouth open, his breathing clear.

∽

I must describe him first. What he looks like. I can do that for, though not yet seventeen, his features appear to have settled. I have long regarded him as unchanging, as one who will never change.

His slightly stooping figure, fierce frame craned forwards in submission. His flat skull. His face—coarse, thick, obtuse. The pimples sprouting on his cheeks and forehead. The black beginnings of a beard. His close-cropped hair. His spectacles.

I know very well—will even proclaim in advance—that people think he is feeble-minded; it is the general opinion, and my daughters share it. As for myself, I am ready to concede the fact, for it contains nothing to betray *me,* after all, nor to reflect upon the soundness of my senses. I have read scientific literature on the subject and I assure you: it is a mere accident. Moreover, he does not resemble me in the least, and barring a certain ferocity, we two have nothing in common. I am completely unafraid therefore, and yet for all that I insist he is a borderline case. He hovers on the border. The proof? His eyes. I am the only person to have frequent occasion for looking into his eyes, and I say at times (though rarely, I admit) something lights up in them, a dark, penetrating vitality.

And not his eyes alone.

And yet . . .

He was born late in my life. Born accidentally, by mistake, by some accursed miracle, for we were both, his mother and I, on the threshold of old age by then.

I have a vivid recollection of that time, the time before he was born. A gentle spring, very long, very wonderful. And I, a poet with five published volumes of verse behind me, resolved to stop writing, resolved with absolute, irrevocable conviction, out of utter despair. For it was only during that spring that I had come to admit to myself that I ought to keep silent.

I had lost the melody.

My closest friends had already started to taunt and to discourage me, dismissing everything I wrote. The young poets and their new poetry bewildered, maddened me. I tried to imitate them secretly and managed to produce the worst I ever wrote. "Well then," I said, "I shall keep silent from now on . . . " and what of it? As a result of this silence, however, our daily routine was disrupted. Sometimes we would go to bed in the early hours of the evening, at others spend half the night in crowded cafés, useless lectures, or at gatherings of aged artists gasping for honors at death's door.

That long, wonderful spring, filled with gentle breezes, bursting with blossoms. And I, roaming the streets, up and down, swept by excitement and despair, feeling doomed. Vainly I tried to get drunk, proclaim my vow of silence to all, repudiating poetry, jesting about poems computed by machines, scornful, defiant, laughing a great deal, chattering, making confessions. And at night writing letters to the papers about trivial matters (public transportation, etc.), polishing my phrases, taking infinite pains with them.

Then, suddenly, this unexpected pregnancy.

This disgrace.

We found out about it in early summer. At first we walked a great deal, then shut ourselves up at home, finally becoming apologetic. First we apologized to the girls, who watched the swelling figure of their elderly mother with horror, then to the relatives come to cast silent looks at the newborn infant.

(The birth occurred one freezing day in midwinter. The tufts of grass in our garden were white with frost.)

We were imprisoned with the baby now. (The girls would not lift a finger for him and deliberately went out more than ever.) We two wanted to speak, tell each other: What a wonderful thing, this birth. But our hearts were not in it, quite clearly. Those sleep-drunken night trips once more, the shadow of the tree streaking the walls, damp, heavy nappies hanging up through all the rooms, all of it depressing. We dragged our feet.

Slowly, sluggishly, it grew, the child, late in everything, sunk in a kind of stupor. Looking back now I see him as a gray fledgling, twitching his weak limbs in the cot by my bed.

The first suspicion arose as late as the third year of his life. It was the girls who broached it, not I. He was retarded in his movements, he was stuttering badly, unprepossessing—hence the girls declared him feeble-minded. And friends would come and scan his face, looking for signs to confirm what we dared not utter.

I do not remember that period in his life very well. His mother's illness took up most of my time. She was fading fast. Nothing had remained of her after that late birth but her shell. We had to look on while she withdrew from us into the desert, forced to wander alone among barren, arid hills and vanish in the twilight.

Each day marked its change in her.

The child was six when his mother died. Heavy, awkward, not attached to anyone in the household, withdrawn into himself but never lost in dreams—anything but a dreamy child. Tense, always, and restless. He trembled if I ran my fingers through his hair.

If I could say with pity: an orphan. But the word sticks in my throat. His mother's dying left no impression, even though, due to my own distraction, he trailed behind us to her funeral. He never asked about her, as though he understood that her going was final. Some months after her death, moreover, every one of her photographs disappeared, and when we discovered the loss a few days later it did not occur to us to question him. When we did, finally, it was too late. The light was fading when he led us to the burial place; in a far corner of the garden, beneath the poplar, among the traces of an old abandoned lime pit, wrapped in an old rag—the slashed pictures.

He stood there in front of us a long time, stuttering fiercely, his small eyes scurrying.

Yet nothing was explained . . .

For the first time our eyes opened and we saw before us a little human being.

I could not restrain myself and I beat him, for the first time since he was born. I seized his wrist and slapped him hard in the face. Then the girls beat him. (Why did they beat him?)

He did not understand . . .

He was startled by the beating. Afterwards he flung himself down and wept. We pulled him to his feet and dragged him home.

I had never realized before how well he knew the house, how thoroughly he had possessed himself of every corner. He had collected his mother's pictures out of obsolete albums, had invaded old envelopes. He had even found a secret spot in the garden that I did not know of. We had lived in this house for many years and I had spent many troubled nights pacing up and down this small garden, but I had never noticed the old extinguished lime—pale, tufted with gray lichen.

Were these the first signs? I do not know. None of us, neither I nor the girls, were prepared to understand at the time. All we feared was the shame or scandal he might bring down on us. Hiding him was impossible, but we wanted at least to protect him.

You see—the girls were single still . . .

In September I entered him in the first year of a school in the suburbs; and during his first week at school I left work early in order to wait for him at the school gate. I was afraid the children would make fun of him.

Noon, and he would be trudging by my side under the searing September sky, his hand in mine. The new satchel lashed to his back, cap low over his forehead, lips slightly parted, the faint mutter of his breathing, his eyes looking at the world nakedly, without detachment, never shifting the angle of his inner vision.

Acquaintances waved their hats at me, came over, shook my hand, bent over him, took his little hand, pressed it. They tried to smile. His dull upward glance froze them. Imbecile, utter imbecile.

After a week I let him come home by himself. My fears had been uncalled for. The children did not need to take the trouble to isolate him—he was isolated to begin with.

The girls were married that year. On the same day, hastily, as though urged on to it, as though they wished to flee the house. And they were so young still.

A year of turmoil. Not a week went by without some sort of revelry in the house. With tears in their eyes the girls would demand that I hide him, and weakness made me comply. I would take him out and we would wander through streets, fields, along the beach.

We did not talk. We watched sunsets, the first stars; rather, I watched and he would stand by my side, motionless, his eyes on the ground. But then the rains came and turned the fields into mud and we were forced to stay indoors. The two suitors had appeared on our horizon, followed by their friends and by their friends' friends, and the whole house went up in smoke and laughter. We tried hiding him in the maid's room, but when he could not sleep we would sneak him into the kitchen. There he would sit in his pajamas and watch people coming and going, then get up and wipe the cutlery; just the spoons at first, then they let him do the knives as well.

Gradually he gained access to the drawing room, the center of commotion. Serving sweets or biscuits to begin with, then filling glasses and offering lighted matches. First, people would draw back at the sight of him. A brief hush would fall upon the room, a kind of sweet horror. One of the suitors would start up angrily from his seat to go and stand by the dark window, seeking refuge in the gloom. Nothing would be audible in the silent room but the child's excited breathing as he moved from one to another with a hard, painful solemnity, his tray held out before him. No one ever refused to take a sweet or a biscuit.

People became used to him in time. The girls softened towards him and tolerated his presence. His small services became indispensable. And when, late in the evening, everybody would be overcome with lassitude, his own face would assume a new light. One of the guests, flushed with drink, might show a sudden interest in him, pull him close, and talk to him at length. The child would go rigid in his grip, his eyes dumb. Then he would go to empty ashtrays.

By the end of that summer we two were alone in the house.

The girls were married one afternoon in mid-August. A large canopy was put up in our garden beneath a deep blue sky. Desiccated thorns rustled beneath the feet of dozens of friends who had gathered there. For some reason I was suffocating with emotion. Something had snapped within me. I was tearful, hugging, kissing everybody. The child was not present at the wedding. Someone, one of the bridegrooms perhaps, had seen to it that he be absent, and he was brought back late in the evening. The last of my friends were tearing themselves from my embrace when my eye suddenly caught sight of him. He was sitting by one of the long tables, dressed in his everyday clothes except for a red tie that someone had put around his neck. A huge slice of cake had been thrust into his hand, the soiled tablecloth had slipped down over his knees. He was chewing listlessly, his eyes on the yellow moon tangled in the branches of our tree.

I went over and gently touched his head.

Flustered, he dropped the cake.

I said: "That moon . . . To be sure, a beautiful moon . . ."

He looked up at the moon as though he had not seen it before.

Thus our life together began, side by side in the quiet house with flasks of perfume and torn handkerchiefs still strewn about. I—a poet fallen silent; he—a feeble-minded, lonely child.

Because it was that, his loneliness, that he faced me with.

I understand that now.

The fact that he was lonely at school goes without saying. During his very first week at school he had retreated to the bench at the back of the classroom, huddling in a corner, a place where he would stay for good, cut off from the rest of his class, the teachers already having considered him hopeless.

All his report cards were inscribed "no evaluation possible," with the hesitant scrawl of a teacher's signature trailing at the bottom of the sheet. I still wonder how they let him graduate from one class to the next. For though occasionally he would be kept back in a class for a second or even a third year, he still crawled forwards, at the slow pace they set him. Perhaps they were indulging me. Perhaps there were some teachers there who liked my old poems.

Mostly I tried to avoid them.

They did their best to avoid me too.

I do not blame them.

If we were nevertheless forced to meet, on parents' day, I always preferred to come late, to come last, with the school building wrapped in darkness and the weary teachers collapsing on their chairs in front of empty classrooms strewn like battlefields and illuminated by naked bulbs.

Then I would appear stealthily at the door, my felt hat crumpled in my hand. My long white mane (for I had kept my mane) would cause any parent still there—a young father or mother—to rise from their seat and leave. The teachers would glance up at me, hold out a limp hand, and offer a feeble smile.

I would sit down and face them.

What could they tell me that I did not know?

Sometimes they forgot who I was.

"Yes sir, whose father please?"

And I would say the name, a sudden throb contracting my chest.

They would leaf through their papers, pull out his blank card and, closing their eyes, head on hand, would demand severely: "How long?"

Meaning, how long could they keep him since it was a hopeless case.

I would say nothing.

They would grow angry. Perhaps the darkness outside would increase their impatience. They insist I take him off their hands. Where to? They do not know. Somewhere else.

An institution perhaps . . .

But gradually their indignation would subside. They admit he is not dangerous. Not disturbing in the least. No, on the contrary, he is always rapt, always listens with a singularly grave attention, his gaze fixed on the teacher's eyes. Apparently, he even tries to do his homework.

I crumple my hat to a pulp. I steal a look at the classroom, floor littered with peel, torn pages, pencil shavings. On the blackboard—madmen's drawings. Minute tears prick my eyes. In plain words I promise to help the child, to work with him every evening. Because we must not give up hope. Because the child is a borderline case, after all.

But in the evenings at home I yield to despair. I spend hours with him in front of the open book and get nowhere. He sits rigidly by my side, never stirring, but my words float like oil on the waves. When I let him go at last he returns to his room and spends about half an hour doing his homework by himself. Then he shuts his exercise books, places them in his schoolbag, and locks it.

Sometimes of a morning when he is still asleep I open the bag and pry into his exercise books. I look aghast at the answers he supplies—remote fantasies; am startled by his sums—outlandish marks traced with zeal and beyond all logic.

But I say nothing. I do not complain about him. As long as he gets up each morning to go mutely to school, to sit on the bench at the back of the classroom.

He would tell me nothing about his day at school. Nor would I ask. He comes and goes, unspeaking. There was a brief period, during his fifth or sixth year at school, I think, when the children bullied him. It was as though they had suddenly discovered him and promptly they began to torment him. All the children of his class, the girls not excepted, would gather around him during break and pinch his limbs as though wishing to satisfy themselves that he really existed, flesh and blood, no specter. He continued going to school all the same, as indeed I insisted that he do.

After a few weeks they gave it up and left him alone once more.

One day he came home from school excited. His hands were dusted with chalk. I assumed he had been called to the blackboard but he said no. That evening he came to me on his own and told me he had been appointed class monitor.

A few days went by. I inquired whether he was still monitor and he said yes. A fortnight later he was still holding the post. I asked whether he enjoyed his duties or whether he found them troublesome. He was perfectly content. His eyes had lit up, his expression became more intent. In my morning searches of his bag I would discover, next to bizarre homework, bits of chalk and a rag or two.

I have an idea that from then on he remained monitor till his last day at school, and a close relationship developed between him and the school's caretaker. In later years they even struck up some sort of friendship. From time to time the caretaker would call him into his cubicle and favor him with a cup of tea left by one of the teachers. It is unlikely that they ever held a real conversation, but a contact of sorts was established.

One summer evening I happened to find myself in the neighborhood of his school and I felt an impulse to go and get acquainted with this caretaker. The gate was shut and I wormed my way through a gap in the fence. I wandered along the dark empty corridors till I came at last upon the caretaker's cubicle, tucked away under the stairs. I went down the few steps and saw him.

He was sitting on a bunk, his legs gathered under him, darkness around. A very short, swarthy person deftly polishing the copper tray on his knees.

I took off my hat, edged my way into the cubicle, mumbled the child's name. He did not move, did not appear surprised, as though he had taken it for granted that I would come one night. He looked up at me and then, suddenly, without a word, he began to smile. A quiet smile, spreading all over his face.

I said: "You know my son."

He nodded, the smile still flickering over his face. His hands continued their work on the tray.

I asked: "How is he? A good boy . . ."

His smile froze, his hands drooped. He muttered something and pointed at his head.

"Poor kid . . . crazy . . ."

And resumed his calm scrutiny of my face.

I stood before him in silence, my heart gone cold. Never before had I been so disappointed, never lost hope so. He returned to his polishing. I backed out without a word.

None of this means to imply that I was already obsessed by the child as far back as that, already entangled with him. Rather the opposite, perhaps. I would be distant with him, absent-minded, thinking of other things.

Thinking of myself.

Never had I been so wrapped up in myself.

In the first place, my silence. This, my ultimate silence. Well, I had maintained it. And it had been so easy. Not a line had I written. True, an obscure yearning might well up in me sometimes. A desire. I whispered to myself, for instance: autumn. And again, autumn.

But that is all.

Friends tackled me. Impossible, they said . . . You are hatching something in secret . . . You have a surprise up your sleeve.

And, strangely excited, I would smile and insist: "No, nothing of the kind. I have written all I want to."

First they doubted, at last they believed me. And my silence was accepted—in silence. It was mentioned only once. Somebody (a young person) published some sort of résumé in the paper. He mentioned me *en passant,* disparagingly, calling my silence sterility. Twice in the same paragraph he called me that—sterile.

Then he let me off.

But I did not care. I felt placid.

This wasteland around me . . .

Dry desert . . .

Rocks and refuse . . .

In the second place, old age was overtaking me. I never imagined that it would come to this. As long as I move about town I feel at ease. But in the evenings after supper I slump into my armchair, a book or paper clutched in my lap, and in a while I feel myself lying there as though paralyzed, half dead. I rise, torture myself out of my clothes, receive the recurring shock of my aging legs, drag myself to bed, and bundle up my body in the clothes, scattering the detective novels that I have begun to read avidly of late.

The house breathes silence. A lost, exhausted tune drifts up from the radio. I read. Slowly, unwittingly, I turn into a large moss-covered rock. Midnight, the radio falls silent, and after midnight the books slip off my knees. I must switch the silent radio off and rid myself of the light burning in the room. It is then that my hour comes, my fearful hour. I drop off the bed like a lifeless body; bent over, racked by pain, staggering, I reach for the switches with my last strength.

One night, at midnight, I heard his steps in the hall. I must mention here that he was a restless sleeper. He used to be haunted by bad dreams that he was never able to relate. He had a night-light by his bed, therefore, and when he woke he would go straight for the kitchen tap and gulp enormous quantities of water, which would calm his fears.

That night, after he had finished drinking and was making his way back to bed, I called him to my room and told him to turn off the light and the radio. I still remember his shadow outlined at the darkened doorway. All of a sudden it seemed to me that he had grown a lot, gained flesh. The light behind him silhouetted his mouth, slightly agape.

I thanked him.

The following night he started prowling through the house again about midnight. I lay in wait for his steps and called him to put out the light once more.

And every night thereafter . . .

Thus his services began to surround me. I became dependent upon them. It started with the light and sound that he would rid me of at midnight and was followed by other things. How old was he? Thirteen, I think . . .

Yes, I remember now. His thirteenth birthday occurred about that time and I made up my mind to celebrate it, for up till then I had passed over all his birthdays in silence. I had planned it to be a real party, generous, gay. I called up his class teacher myself and contacted the other teachers as well. I invited everybody. I sent invitations in his name to all his classmates.

True, all the children in his class were younger than he. Hardly eleven yet.

On the appointed Saturday, in the late morning, after a long and mortifying wait, a small band of ten sniggering boys showed up at our place waving small parcels wrapped in white paper. Not a single teacher had troubled himself to come. None of the girls had dared.

They all shook hands with me, very much embarrassed, very much amazed at the sight of my white hair (one of them asked in a whisper: "That his grandfather?"), and entered timidly into the house, which none of them had visited before. They scrutinized me with great thoroughness and were relieved when they found me apparently sane.

The presents were unwrapped.

It emerged that everyone had brought the same: a cheap pencil-case worth a few pennies at most. All except one curly-headed, rather pale boy, a poetic type, who came up brazenly with an old, rusted pocketknife—albeit a big one with many blades—which for some reason excited general admiration.

All the presents were accompanied by more or less uniform, conventional notes of congratulation. The little poet of the pocketknife had added a few pleasing rhymes.

He accepted his presents silently, terribly tense.

It surprised me that no one had brought a book.

As though they had feared he might not be able to read it . . .

I waited on them myself, taking great pains with each. I served sandwiches, cake, sweets, and lemonade, then ice cream. They sat scattered around the drawing room, embedded in armchairs and couches, munching sweets, not speaking. Their eyes roved around the room incessantly, examining the place as though suspicious of it. Occasionally tittering among themselves for no good reason.

My boy was sitting forlornly in a corner of the room, more like a visitor than the guest of honor at his own party. He was munching too, but his eyes were lowered.

I thought my presence might be hampering the children and left them. And indeed, soon after I had gone, the tension relaxed. Laughter began to bubble up in the room. When I returned after a while I found them all with their shoes off, romping on the carpet, jumping up and down on the couch. He was not among them. I went to look for him and found him on the kitchen balcony, cleaning their shoes.

He said: "I am the monitor."

Thus ended his birthday party. Their clothes in wild disarray, stifling their laughter, they put on their shoes, then rose to face me, shook my hand once more, and were off, leaving nine pencil-cases behind them. As for the old pocketknife that had aroused so much admiration, the little poet who had brought it asked there and then to borrow it for a week and apparently never returned it.

It is in self-defense that I offer these details, since before a fortnight had passed he was polishing my shoes as well. I simply left them on the balcony and found them polished. He did it willingly, without demur. And it became a custom—his and mine. Other customs followed.

Taking my shoes off, for instance. I come back from work late in the afternoon, sink down on the bench in the hall to open my mail. He appears from one of the rooms, squats at my feet, unties the laces, pulls off my shoes, and replaces them with slippers.

And that relieves me to some extent.

I suddenly discover there is strength in his arms, compared with the ebbing strength in mine. Whenever I fumble with the lid of a jar, fail to extricate a nail from the wall, I call upon him. I tell him: "You are young and strong and I am growing weaker. Soon I'll die."

But I must not joke with him. He does not digest banter. He stands aghast, his face blank.

He is used to emptying the rubbish bin, has done it since he was eight. He runs my errands readily, fetches cigarettes, buys a paper. He has time at his disposal. He spends no more than half an hour on his homework. He has no friends, reads no books, slouches for hours in a chair gazing at the wall or at me. We live in a solid, quiet neighborhood. All one sees through the window are trees and a fence. A peaceful street. What is there for him to do? Animals repel him. I brought him a puppy once and a week later he lost it. Just lost it and showed no regret. What is there for him to do? I teach him to tidy up the house, show him where everything belongs. He catches on slowly but eventually he learns to arrange my clothes in the cupboard, gather up the papers and books strewn over the floor. In the mornings I would leave my bedclothes rumpled and when I returned at night everything would be in order, strictly in order.

Sometimes I fancy that everything is in readiness for a journey. That there is nothing to be done but open a suitcase, place the curiously folded clothes inside, and go forth. One day I had to go on a short trip up north, and within half an hour of informing him he had a packed suitcase standing by the door with my walking stick on top.

Yes, I have got myself a stick lately. And I take it along with me wherever I go, even though I have no need of it yet. When I stop to talk with people in the street I insert it in the nearest available crack and put my whole weight on its handle. He sharpens the point from time to time to facilitate the process.

To such lengths does he go in his care of me.

At about that time he also learned to cook. The elderly cleaning woman who used to come in now and then taught him. At first he would cook for himself and eat alone before I came back from work, but in time he would prepare a meal for me too. A limited, monotonous menu, somewhat lacking in flavor, but properly served. He had unearthed a china service in the attic. It had been a wedding present, an elaborate set containing an assortment of golden-edged plates decorated with flowers, cherubs, and butterflies. He put it into use. He would place five different-sized plates, one on top of the other, in front of me, add a quantity of knives and forks, and wait upon me with an air of blunt insistence.

Where had he learned all that?

It transpired that a story about a king's banquet had been read in class.

I am roused.

"What king?"

He does not remember the name.

"Other heroes?"

He doesn't remember.

I ask him to tell the story, at least.

He starts, and stops again at once. It has become muddled in his head.

His eyes cloud over. The first pimples have sprouted on his cheeks.

A thought strikes me: viewed from a different angle he might fill one with terror.

At night he assists me in my bath. I call him in to soap my back and he enters on tiptoe, awed by my nakedness in the water, picks up the sponge, and passes it warily over my neck.

When I wish to reciprocate and wait upon him in turn, nothing comes of it. Arriving home I announce: Tonight I am going to prepare supper! It appears supper is served already. I wish to help him in his bath, and it appears he has bathed already.

I therefore take him with me at night to meetings with friends, to artists' conventions, for I still belong to all the societies and unions. I have accustomed people to his presence and they notice him no more, much as I do not notice their shadow.

He always sits in the last row, opening doors for latecomers, helping them out of their coats, hanging them up. People take him for one of the attendants, and indeed, he is inclined to attach himself to these. I find him standing near a group of ushers, listening grim-eyed to their talk. At times I find him exchanging words with the charwoman who stands leaning on her broom.

What does he say to her? I am never able to guess.

Does he love me? How can one tell. Something in my behavior seems to frighten him. Perhaps it is my age, perhaps my silence. Whatever it is, he carries himself in my presence as one expecting a blow.

Strange, for there is peace between us. The days pass tranquilly and I imagined this tranquillity would last out our life together, till the day I would have to part from him, that is. I thought, how fortunate that in this silence of mine I am confronted by a boy of such feeble brains, on the border, and far from me.

True, I am sometimes overcome by restlessness, possessed by a desire to cling to somebody. Then I rush off to Jerusalem and surprise my daughters with a visit of an hour or two.

They receive me affectionately, hang on to my neck and hug me hard. And while we stand there in a clinging embrace their husbands look on, a faint expression of contempt in their eyes. Afterwards we sit down and chat, bandying about the kind of word play and witticisms that irritate the husbands. Still, they utter no word of complaint, knowing full well that I won't stay, that if I come like a whirlwind—so I go. After an hour or two I rouse myself for a speedy departure, still harboring the dregs of my passion. They all urge me to prolong my visit, stay, spend the night, but I never do. I must go home to the boy, I argue, as though his entire existence depended upon me. More kissing and hugging follows; then the husbands take me to the station. We rarely speak during the short ride. We have nothing to say to each other. Besides, I am still suspect in their eyes. This white mane flowing down my neck, the stick jiggling in my hand. I am still some sort of a poet to them. The volumes of my poetry, I know, have a place of honor in their drawing-room bookcase. I cannot prevent that.

At such a time I prefer the child's dumb look.

In the winter there are times when I draw the bolts at six. What do I do in the hours left till bedtime? I read the papers, listen to the radio, thumb the pages of books. Time passes and I make my bargain with boredom in private.

In the summer I often walk back and forth along the beach or aimlessly through the streets. I am likely to stand in front of a building under construction for hours on end, lost in thought.

Trivial thoughts . . .

Years ago I would carry little notebooks with me wherever I went. Working myself up into a fever, fanning the flame of creation, rhyming, turning words over and over. Nowadays, not even a pang.

Where is he?

I look through the window and see him in the garden, under a bleak autumn sky. He is pruning the bushes and trees with a savage violence. Lopping off whole branches, tearing at leaves.

He has it in for the old poplar in particular, cuts away with zeal the new shoots that have sprouted at its base, climbs up into the foliage and saws relentlessly. The tree bends and groans.

Sometimes my eyes stay riveted upon him for hours and I cannot bring myself to look away. His intent gravity, his rage. Shadows play over his face, his face which has taken on an absurdly studious quality owing to the thick spectacles he has begun to wear. He was found to be shortsighted.

I know he is trimming off more than is necessary, that he pulls up plants, roots and all, in his vehemence. Still, I do not interfere and go on standing mutely by the window. I would tell myself: what survives will flower in the spring and make up for the damage.

∞

When was the first time? That he found out about my being a poet, I mean. This madness that has taken a hold over us the past year, I mean.

Towards the end of last winter I fell ill and kept him home to nurse me. For several days we were together the whole day long, and he did not move from my side. This was something that had never happened before, for as a rule not a day would pass when I did not go out, wandering, sitting in cafés, visiting people.

I was feverish and confined to bed, dozing fitfully, eyes fluttering. He moved about the house or sat by the door of my room, his head turned in my direction. Occasionally I would ask for tea, and he would rouse himself, go to the kitchen, and return with a steaming cup.

The light was dying slowly, gray sky flattening the windows. We did not turn on the lights for my illness had made my eyes sensitive.

The silence lay large between us. Could I hold a conversation with him?

I asked whether he had prepared his homework.

He nodded his head from his corner of the room.

What could I talk to him about?

I asked about his monitorship. He replied with yes and no and with shakes of his head.

At last I grew tired. I let my head drop back on the pillow and closed my eyes. The room grew darker. Outside it began to drizzle. During those days of illness my mind had started to wander with fantasies. Fantasies about the bed. I would imagine it to be a white, violent country of sweeping mountains and streaming rivers, and me exploring it.

Then such utter calm. The warmth of the bed enveloping each cell in my body.

I started at the sound of his harsh voice, sudden in the trickling silence.

"What do you do?"

I opened my eyes. He was sitting by the door, his eyes on my face.

I raised myself a little, astonished.

"What? What do you mean? Now? Well, what? I'm dozing . . ."

"No, in general . . . " and he turned away as though sorry he had asked.

In a while I understood. He was asking about my profession.

Had they been discussing "professions" in class?

He did not know . . .

I tell him what my profession is (I am employed by a newspaper-clipping bureau), but he finds it difficult to understand. I explain at length. Suddenly he has understood. There is no reaction. He seems a little disappointed. Hard to say why. He cannot have formed the idea in his feeble mind that I am a pilot or a sailor, can he? Did he think I was a pilot or a sailor?

No.

What did he think?

He didn't think.

Silence again. He sits forlorn in the corner, a sad, somber figure. His spectacles gleam in the twilight. It rains harder now, the old poplar huddles in the garden, wet with tears. Suddenly I cannot bear his grief. I sit up in bed, eyes open in the dark, and tell him in a low voice that, as a matter of fact, I used to have another occupation. I wrote poetry. You see, Father used to be a poet. They must have learned about poets in class. And I get out of bed in a fever of excitement, cross the dark room in my bare feet, light a small lamp, cross back to the bookcase, pluck my books one by one from the shelves.

He watches me in silence, his spectacles slightly askew, hands limp on the arms of his chair.

I grasp his wrist, pull him up, and stand him before me.

Dry-handed I open my books in their hard covers. The small, untouched pages move with a faint crackle. Black lines of print on pale paper flit before my eyes. Words like: *autumn, rain, gourd.*

He remains unmoved, does not stir, his eyes are cast down, motionless. An absolute moron.

I sent him out of the room. I gathered my books and took them with me to bed. The light stayed on in my room till dawn. All night I lay groping for the sweet pain passionately poured into ancient poems. Words like: *bread, path, ignominy.*

The next day my fever had abated somewhat and I sent him off to school. My books I thrust back among the others. I was convinced he had understood nothing. A few days later, though, discovering all five volumes ranged neatly side by side, I realized something had penetrated. But it was little as yet.

That was his final school year, though the fact marked no change in his habits. He still spent about half an hour a day on his homework, wrote whatever it was he wrote, closed his exercise books, locked his bag, and turned to his household chores. In class he kept to his remote corner, but his attendance at lessons had dwindled. The caretaker would call upon him time and again. To help store away stoves in the attic or repair damaged furniture in the cellar.

When he was present in class he would sit there rapt as ever, his eyes, unwavering, on the teacher.

The final days of the school year, their slack atmosphere . . .

Two or three weeks before the end of term a poem of mine was taught in class. The last pages of the textbook contained a collection of many different poems, some sort of anthology for every season, for a free period or such. An old poem of mine, written dozens of years ago, was among them. I had not aimed it at youth, but people mistook its intention.

The teacher read it out to the class. Then she explained the difficult words and finally let one of the pupils read it. And that was all there was to it. My son might have paid no attention to the occurrence from his bench had the teacher not pointed him out to say: "But yes, that is his father . . ."

The remark did nothing to improve the child's standing in class, let alone enhance the poem's distinction. In any case, by the end of the lesson both poem and poet were no doubt forgotten.

Apparently, however, the boy did not forget; he remained aglow. Possibly he wandered by himself through the empty classroom, picking up peel, wiping the blackboard, excited.

Coming back from work that evening I found the house in darkness. I opened the front door and saw him waiting in the unlit hall. He could not contain his passion. He threw himself at me, bursting into a kind of savage wail, nearly suffocating me. And without letting me take off my jacket, undo my tie, he dragged me by the hand into one of the rooms, switched on the light, opened the textbook, and began reading my poem in a hoarse voice. Mispronouncing vowels, slurring words, bungling the stresses.

I was stunned in the face of this turbulent emotion. Compassion welled up in me. I pulled him close and stroked his hair. It was evident that he had still not grasped what the poem was about, even though it was not rich in meaning.

He held my sleeve in a hard grip and asked when had I written the poem.

I told him.

He asked to see other poems.

I pointed at my volumes.

He wanted to know whether that was all.

Smiling I showed him a drawer of my bureau stuffed with a jumble of poems and fragments, little notebooks I used to carry on my person and have with me always.

He asked whether I had written any new poems today. Now I burst out laughing. His blunt face raised up to me in adoration, this evening hour, and I still in my jacket and tie.

I told him that I had stopped writing before he was born and that the contents of that drawer should have been thrown out long ago.

I took off my jacket, loosened my tie, sat down to unlace my shoes.

He fetched my slippers.

His expression was despondent.

As though he had received fearful tidings.

I burst into laughter again.

I made a grab for his clipped hair and jerked his head with a harsh affection.

I, who would shrink from touching him.

A few days later I found the drawer wrenched open, empty. Not one scrap of paper left. I caught him in the garden weeding the patch beneath the tree with a hoe. Why had he done it? He thought I did not need them. He was just cleaning out. And hadn't I said myself I wasn't writing anymore.

Where were all the papers?

He had thrown out the written ones, and the little notebooks he had sold to a hawker.

I beat him. For the second time in my life, and again in the garden, by the poplar. With all the force of my old hands I slapped his rough cheeks with their soft black down.

He trembled all over . . .

His fists closed white-knuckled and desperate over the hoe. He could have hit back. He was strong enough to knock me down.

But then, abruptly, my anger died. The entire affair ceased to be important. Relics of old poems, lost long ago. Why the trembling? Why, with my silence sealed?

Once more I believed the affair ended. I never imagined it was but the beginning.

Long summer days. Invariably blue. Once in a while a tiny cloud sails on its sleepy journey from one horizon to the other. All day flocks of birds flop down upon our poplar, screaming, beating the foliage.

Evenings—a dark devouring red.

The child's last day at school.

A day later: the graduation ceremony and presentation of diplomas.

He did not receive one, of course. He ascended the platform with the other pupils nonetheless, dressed in a white shirt and khaki trousers (he was about seventeen years old). And sat in the full, heavy afternoon light listening gravely to the speeches. When it was the turn of the caretaker to be thanked he lifted his eyes and began a heavy, painstaking examination of the audience to search him out.

I kept myself concealed at the back of the hall behind a pile of chairs, my hat on my knees. The speeches ended and a short artistic program began.

Two plump girls mounted the stage and announced in voices shrill with emotion that they would play a sonata by an anonymous composer who lived hundreds of years ago. They then seated themselves behind a creaking piano and beat out some melancholy chords with four hands.

Stormy applause from enraptured parents.

A small boy with pretty curls dragged an enormous cello onto the stage and he, too, played a piece by an anonymous composer (a different one, apparently).

I closed my eyes.

I liked the idea of all this anonymity.

A storm of applause from enraptured parents.

Suddenly I became aware of someone's eyes upon me. Glancing around I saw, a few steps away, the caretaker, sprawled on a chair, dressed in his overalls. He made a gentle gesture with his head.

Two girls and two boys came on stage and began reciting. A story, a humorous sketch, two or three poems.

At the first sound of rhymes my boy rose suddenly from his place and began a frantic search for me. The audience did not understand what that spectacled, dumb-faced boy standing up at the back of the stage might possibly be looking for. His fellow pupils tried to pull him down, but in vain. He was seeking me, his eyes hunting through the hall. The rhymes rang in his ears, swaying him. He wanted to shout. But he could not find me. I had dug myself in too well behind the chairs, hunched low.

As soon as the ceremony was over I fled. He arrived home in the evening. It turned out he had been helping the caretaker arrange the chairs in the hall.

The time had come to decide his fate. I reiterate: He verges on the border. A borderline child. Haven't I let the time slip by? Do I still possess my hold over him?

For the time being he stayed at home with me, took care of his father, and began to occupy himself with poems.

Yes, he turned his hand to poetry.

It turned out that those poetry remnants of mine, the little notebooks, thin little pages, were still in his possession. Neither thrown out nor sold. He had lied to me there by the poplar.

I did not find out all at once. At first he contrived to keep them hidden from me. But gradually I became aware of them. Scraps of paper began to flit about the house, edges sticking out of his trouser pockets, his bedclothes. He introduced a new habit. Whenever I sent him on an errand he took out a piece of paper and wrote down the nature of the errand in his slow, elaborate, childish script full of spelling mistakes.

"Oblivion o'ercomes me," he suddenly informed me one day.

My walking stick had split and I had asked him to take it for repair. At once he extracted a little notebook, one of those old notebooks I used to cherish, used to carry in my pocket in order to scribble the first draft of a poem, a line, the scrap of an idea.

I felt my throat contract, sweat break out. My hand reached for the notebook as of itself. He surrendered it instantly. I leafed through with a feeble hand. White pages, the ragged remains of many others torn out. Then a single, disjointed line in my hurried scrawl: *"Oblivion o'ercomes me."* And then more empty pages, their edges crumpled.

Peace returned to me. He wished to leave the little notebook in my hands but I insisted that he take it back.

He went off.

Up in his room I rifled through his desk but found nothing. Then I took my mind off the whole thing. In the evening I found a yellowed piece of paper on my bureau and written on it in my indecipherable script: *This azure sky's the match of man.*

And the words "azure sky" crossed out with a faint line.

I swept up to his room and there he sat, huddled in a corner, waiting for me in dull anticipation. I folded the paper in front of his eyes, placed it on his desk, and left the room. The following evening, after supper, I once again found two forgotten lines on my bureau.

Futile again before thee.
This long slow winter.

And this one I had already torn up.

And the day after, a slanting line in tortuous script: *My lunacy in my pale seed.*

And harsh, violent erasures around the words.

And beside the torn-out page a red carnation from the garden in a small vase.

Here now, I must tell about the flowers.

For the house became filled with flowers. Old, forgotten vases came down from shelves and storeroom and were filled with flowers. He would gather buttercups on his way, pick them between the houses, steal into parks for carnations, and pilfer roses from private gardens. The house filled with a hot, heavy scent. Yellow stamens scattered over tables, crumbled on carpets.

Sheets of paper were always lying on my bureau; sharpened pencils across.

In this way, with the obstinacy of his feeble mind, he tried to tempt me back to writing poems.

At first I was amused. I would pick up the little pages, read, and tear them up; would smell the flowers. With the sharpened pencils I would draw dotted lines and sign my name a thousand times in the little notebooks.

But soon this mania of his became overwhelming.

Those pages uprooted from my notebooks would pursue me all over the house. I never knew there had been so much I had wanted to write. He placed them between the pages of books I read, in my briefcase, beneath my bedside lamp, beside the morning paper, between the cup and saucer, near the toothpaste. When I pulled out my wallet a scrap of paper would flutter down.

I read and tore up and threw out.

As yet I made no protest. I was intrigued, curious to read what went through my mind in those far-off days. And there was bound to be an end to those little pages. For this much I knew: there *was* an end to them.

Late at night, when I had long been buried under my bedclothes, I would hear his bare feet paddling through the house. Planting pages filled with my personal untidy scrawl. Twisted, entangled letters, scattered words thickly underscored.

We maintained our wonted silence. And day after day he collected the torn-up scraps from ashtrays and wastepaper baskets.

Except that the flow of notes was ebbing. One morning I found a page on my desk with a line written in his handwriting striving to imitate mine. Next morning it was his hand again, stumbling awkwardly over the clean page.

And the flowers filling every room . . .

And the sky filling with clouds . . .

My patience gave out. I rebelled. I burst into his room and found him sitting and copying the self-same line. I swept up the remains of all the little notebooks and tore them up before his eyes. I plucked the flowers out of all the vases, piled them up on the doorstep, and ordered him to take them away.

I told him: "These games are over."

He took the flowers, went to bury them in the nearby field, and did not return. He stayed away three days. On the second I ransacked the town in a silent search. (The house filled with dust in the meantime. Dishes piled up in the sink.)

In the afternoon of the third day he came back, suntanned, an outdoor smell in his clothes.

I suppressed my anger, sat him down in front of me.

Where had he been? What done? Why had he run away?

He had slept in the nearby field, not far from home. Whenever I went out he would return and hide in his room. Once I had come in unexpectedly, but had not caught him. Why had he run away? He could not explain. He had thought I wished him out of the way. That I wished to write poetry in lonely seclusion. For that was what they had said at school about poets, about their loneliness . . .

Those accursed teachers.

Or could it be some heavy, some new piece of cunning.

I must decide his fate. He is beginning to waver on the border.

I armed myself with patience, talked to him at length. Well, now what do you want, I said. For I, I have done with writing. I have written my fill. Then what do you want?

He covered his eyes with his palms. Blurted out some hot, stuttering words again. It was hard to follow him. At last I gathered from his confused jumble of words that he believed me unhappy.

You should have seen him.

This feeble-brained boy, boy on the border, his spectacles slipping slowly down his nose. Big. Nearly eighteen.

Late afternoon, an autumn sun roving leisurely about the rooms. Music is coming from the house next door. Someone is practicing scales on a violin. The same exercise, many times over, and out of tune. Only in one key the melody goes off every time into some sort of melancholy whine.

Suddenly I am certain of my death. I can conceive how the grass will go on rustling in this garden.

I look at him and see him as he is. An unfinished piece of sculpture.

Smiling, I whisper, "See, I am tired. Perhaps you could write for me."

He is dumbfounded. He takes off his spectacles, wipes them on his shirt, puts them back.

"I can't," he in a whisper too.

Such despair. Of course he can't. I must cut loose. Ties, tangles. Long years of mortification. One could cry. They left me alone with him. And again that dissonant whine.

"You'll help me," he whispers at me now, as though we were comrades.

"I will not help you."

A great weariness came over me. I stood up, took my hat, and went out, walked twice around the scales player's house and went into town.

In the evening I came back and found him gone. I was obliged to prepare my own supper again and when I was slicing bread the knife slipped. It has been many years since I bled so.

I believed he had run off again, but he returned late at night, my room already dark. He began to prowl about the house, measure it with his steps, back and forth, much as I used to in former days when words would start to struggle up in me.

I fell asleep to the sound of his tread.

Next day he emptied out his room. All his schoolbooks, encyclopedias received as presents, copybooks, everything went out. The sheets of paper and sharpened pencils he transferred to his own desk.

The sky turned dim with autumn.

I began to play with the idea of retirement. Something in the romantic fashion. To give up work, sell the house, collect the money, and escape, far away. Settle in some remote, decaying port. From there to an attic in a big city. In short, plans, follies. I went to travel agencies and was deluged with colorful pamphlets. I affixed a notice to the fence: For Sale.

A light rain fell.

One Friday I went to Jerusalem to see my daughters and spend the Sabbath there.

I received a great welcome. They even lighted candles in my honor and filled the house with flowers. My grandchildren played with the walking stick. I realized I had been neglecting everybody. At dinner they placed me at the head of the table.

I talked all evening about him, obsessively. I did not change the subject, refused to drop it. I demanded a solution for him, insisted he be found some occupation. I announced my plans for going abroad, wandering about the world for a bit. Someone must take charge of him. He can be made use of, too. He may serve someone else. As long as he was taken off my hands. I want my release, at last. He was approaching manhood.

I did not say a word about the poems.

For once the husbands gave me their full attention. The girls were puzzled. What has passed between you two? We rose from the table and transferred to armchairs for coffee. The grandchildren came to say good night in their pajamas. Gesturing with their little hands they recited two verses by a poetess who had died not long ago. Thereupon they put their lips to my face, licked me, and went to bed. I went on talking about him. Impossible to divert me. They were all tired by now, their heads nodding as they listened. From time to time they exchanged glances, as though it were I who had gone mad.

Then they suddenly left me. Promising nothing, leading me gently to bed. They kissed me and went away.

Only then did I discover that a storm had been rising outside all evening. A young tree beat against the window with its many boughs. Thumping on the glass, prodding around the frame. All night it tried to force an entry, to come into my bed. When I woke up in the morning all was calm. A sky of sun and clouds.

The young tree stood still, facing the sun. Nothing but a few torn leaves, bright green leaves that trembled on my windowsill.

I went home in the afternoon. My sons-in-law had promised to find him employment. My daughters talked about a semi-closed institution.

Winter erupted from the soil. Puddles were forming between pavements and road. My reflection rippled and broke into a thousand fragments.

He was not at home. His room was locked. I went out into the yard and peered through the window. The window stood wide open and the room appeared tidy beyond it. The sheets of paper glimmered white on his desk. Something was written on them, surely. I went back into the house and tried to force the door but it would not yield. Back in the yard again I rolled a stone to the wall beneath his window and tried to climb on top of it but failed. My legs began to tremble. I was no longer young. Suddenly I thought: What is he to me? I went in, changed my tie, and went out in search of friends in cafés.

Saturday night. The streets loud. We are crowded in a corner of the café, old, embittered artists, burnt-out volcanoes wrapped in coats. Wheezing smoke, crumbling in our withered hands the world sprung up since last Saturday. Vapors rise from the ground and shroud the large glass front of the café. I sprawl inert on my chair, puffing at a cigarette butt, dancing my stick on the stone floor between my feet. I know. This town is built on sand, dumb and impervious. Under the flimsy layer of houses and pavements—a smothered desert of sand.

Suddenly a crowd of unkempt, hairy bohemians swarm by. A crowd of young fools. We scowl, squint at them. And there is my boy trailing after them, a few paces behind the crowd, his cheeks flushed.

They fling themselves on the chairs of a next-door café. Most of them are drunk. My boy stays on their fringes, huddled in a chair. Some sort of blustering conversation goes on. I do not take my eyes off him. Someone rises, takes a piece of paper out of his pocket, and begins reading a poem. No one is listening to him except my boy. The reader stops in the middle, moves from one to the other, finally hovers intently over the clipped head of my son. A few of them laugh. Someone leans over the boy, pats his cheek . . .

I am certain: nobody knows his name, nor that of his father.

Some minutes later I sit up, take my stick, and go to the beach to look at the dark sea. Then home. I lie on the couch, take the paper, and begin turning its pages. I linger over the literary supplement, read a line or two of a poem, a paragraph in a story—and stop. Literature bores me to tears. Abruptly I fall asleep, as I am, in my clothes. Dream I am taken away for an operation. Being anesthetized and operated on, painlessly. Wakened, anesthetized again, the still flesh dissected. At last I understand: it is the light shining in my face.

I wake, rise, shivering with cold, clothes rumpled. A soft rain outside. I go to the kitchen, put a kettle on, and wait for the water to boil. Piles of dirty dishes tower over me.

A big dilapidated motor car, its headlights off, crawls into our little street at a remarkably slow pace. At last it brakes to a creaking stop in front of our house, beside the lamppost. Loud whooping and howling from inside. A long pause. A door opens and someone is discharged, pale, confused. It is my son. His features are petrified, no shadow of a smile. Another door opens. Someone else scrambles out, staggers into the middle of the road, dead-drunk. He goes over to the boy, grasps his hands, and pumps them up and down affectionately. Then squeezes his way back into the car.

More yells and screams from the imprisoned human mass. A long pause. Then a jerk and a roar, and the blind battered wreck reverses and like some black turtle inches its way backwards out of the street.

My son is standing by the lamppost, at the precise spot where he has been unloaded. For a long time he stands there unmoving, his body slightly bowed. Suddenly he doubles up and vomits. He wipes his mouth with the palm of his hand and strides towards the house. Passes by the kitchen without noticing me, enters his room, and shuts the door. A faint cloud of alcohol floats through the hall.

Winter. With the first touch of rain these lowlands strive to revert to swamp.

An old half-blind poet, who publishes a steady stream of naive, pitiful poems and woos young poets, meets me in the street, links his arm through mine, and walks me round and round under a gray sky, through wet streets. Finally, he informs me with something like a wink that he has met my son in the company of young artists.

"A fine young man. Does he write?"

Rumors reach me from all sides. Some say they torment him. Others say that on the contrary, those degenerate creatures accept him gladly. It isn't every day that they get hold of such a tongue-tied moron. Meanwhile he has become one young poet's minion, and messenger boy to the editor of a literary magazine.

I reproach him with harsh words but he does not listen. Abstract-minded, his eyes flitting over the cloud-hung world, he does not even see me. His face has paled a little over the past few weeks, his blunt features taken on an ascetic, somehow spiritual look. I know: one incautious word on my part, and he will break loose, roam about the streets, and disgrace me. Already he has neglected the house completely. He takes his meals outside. The garden is running to seed. And I had imagined that he felt some tenderness towards the plants.

When at home he shuts himself up in his room and throws himself into writing. We have not seen a single poem yet. But I know beyond question: he writes.

I come up against him in the hall, catch him by the sleeve, and ask mockingly: "Monsieur writes? Yes?"

He wriggles under my hand. My language startles him. He does not understand and looks at me in horror, as though I were beyond hope.

He is capable of staying locked up in his room for hours on end, wonderfully concentrated. Occasionally he enters the drawing room, goes to the bookcase, takes out a volume of poetry or some other book, and stands a long time poring over it. As a rule he never turns over the page. Then he puts the book down quietly and goes out. Of late he has begun referring frequently to the dictionary, digging into it, turning its leaves incessantly like a blind man. I doubt whether he knows how to use it.

I finally come over and ask him what he wants.

He wants to know how to write the sky.

"The sky?"

"The word 'sky'. . . "

"How? What do you mean, how? Just the way it sounds."

That does not help him much. He stands in front of me, fearfully grave.

"With an 'e' after the 'y' or without . . . " he whispers.

"With an 'e'?" I say thunderstruck, "What on earth for?"

He bites his lips.

"With an 'e'?" I repeat, my voice shrilling to a yell. "And, anyway, what do you want with the sky?"

This one remains unanswered. The dictionary closes softly between his hands. He returns to his room. A while later he steals back to the bookcase, takes the dictionary, and starts hunting through it. I jump up.

"What now?"

"Independence . . . " he stammers.

"Independence? Well?"

". . . 'ance' or . . . 'ence'?"

Once again this inexplicable fury. The more so as all of a sudden I do not know myself how to spell *independence*. I pounce upon him, grab the dictionary out of his hands, search feverishly . . .

Meanwhile my retirement plans are taking shape. From time to time people come to inspect the house put up for sale. I show them over the rooms, let them intrude into every corner, take them down to the cellar, around the yard, into the garden, and back to the balcony. In a low voice I recite its merits, this house that I have lived in for thirty years. Then, coolly, I state the price. Before they depart I take down their name and spell out mine in exchange. They bend over the piece of paper and write my name with complete equanimity. Not the faintest ripple of recognition. Haven't they ever read poetry in their lives? I shall apparently leave these regions in complete anonymity.

The garden, however, leaves a bad impression with the buyers. Weeds and mires. The boy refuses to touch a spade. I therefore take up the gardening tools myself and every day I weed out some of the boldest specimens and cover the puddles with them.

A farewell party at the office in my honor. All the office employees assembled an hour before closing time. Cakes were served, glasses raised. I was eulogized at great length. I even saw tears in some eyes. No one mentioned my poetry, as though to avoid hurting my feelings. Finally, a parting gift: an oil painting, a murky sea.

I start packing my bags. Much vacillation in front of the bookcase. What shall I take, what leave? I send off urgent letters to my sons-in-law regarding the boy's fate. I engage them in telephone conversations, prevail upon them to act. Finally they make an appointment to meet me at a small café in town. Sitting round a small table they unfold their plans. They have made inquiries and finally have found an old artisan in a Jerusalem suburb, a bookbinder who has consented to take on the boy as an apprentice. He will be provided with his meals and sleeping quarters. The man used to have just such a child himself, and it died of an illness. He has, however, laid down one condition: Should the boy fall ill he will be returned at once. Like a seizure or some such case . . . On this point they were inexorable: They will not care for him in sickness.

The sons-in-law have therefore made further investigations and found a lone old woman, a few houses away from the bookbinder, who will be prepared to accept him when ill. Against a remuneration, of course . . . Well, and that is all. I must put my signature to both.

And they come out with papers.

I sign at once. Yet a rage flares up in me while I do.

"As far as seizures and sickness are concerned, your trouble was unnecessary. You know he isn't one of those . . . He is a borderline child . . . I have said as much a thousand times . . . But you won't begin to understand . . . Oh well, let it go."

My sons-in-law collect the documents, barring one copy which they leave with me. They gulp the last of their coffee, give me a kindly smile.

"See, and you thought we weren't looking after you . . ."

The day after I sign again, this time to transfer the house to a buyer found at last. When all is said and done, I have received a reasonable sum for it, and that just for the land, since the house itself is going to be demolished.

The furniture was included in the price. Three workmen appeared one day at dusk and began clearing the house. Everything was taken except two mattresses. They even pulled the desk from under him while he sat writing at it. He was outraged. He prowled about the house, his papers fluttering white in his arms. A few slipped to the floor and, by the time he noticed, one of the workmen was already picking them up to wrap the lamp shades in. He threw himself at the man with all the strength of his heavy bulk. Tried to get his teeth into him.

It has struck me that dusk is a time when his senses are overcome by a heavy stupor.

Banknotes fill my drawer. I obtain no more than a quarter of the things' value, but even so the money piles up. I wish to sell everything, and what I can't sell I give away. I have been forcing loads of books on my friends. Were the boy a little less occupied he would sell to his hawkers what I throw out.

We have even been making incursions into the cellar and have dredged up old clothes, brooms, more books, manuscripts—my own and others'—trivia, simulacrums and crumbs and fables. A cloud of dust hovered on the cellar steps for three whole days.

I told my café friends: "Here, this is how a man cuts his bonds."

In addition I still pay regular visits to the tiny harbor of this big town in order to whip up a wanderlust. Wrapped in my overcoat, umbrella in hand, I wander among the cranes, sniffing salt and rust, trying to strike up a conversation with the sailors. I am still deliberating where to go. At first I had considered Europe as my destination, then thought of the Greek islands. I had already entered into negotiations with a Turkish ship captain regarding the Bosphorus when I went and bought, for a ridiculous price, a round-trip ticket on a freighter sailing the sea between this country and Cyprus. I went on board the ship myself and rapped my stick against the door of my prospective cabin.

This journey will be something of a prelude. Afterwards we shall sail away again, further away.

My son writes on throughout, writes standing as though in prayer. His papers are scattered on the windowsill, which serves him as a desk. Beside them lies a small dictionary which he has rescued from the debacle. When I look at his form the thought strikes me: Why thus, just as he is, he may go and sleep with a woman. And who knows? Perhaps he already has. He has not yet taken in the fact of my retirement, my impending departure. He is intent on his own. It was difficult enough to tear him away, one afternoon, and make him accompany me to Jerusalem to see the old bookbinder.

It was a gentle winter day, cloudy but no real rain. In Jerusalem we found the old bookbinder waiting for us at the bus station with a run-down commercial van, unbound books slithering about in the back. He took us to a suburb of the town, to the slope of a narrow, tree-tangled wadi very close to the border. He motioned us into the house in silence, and in silence his wife received us. Tea and cakes were served and we were made to sit by the table.

I was very pleased with them. They scrutinized the boy carefully. Hard to say that he pleased them, but they were visibly relieved, having expected worse. Slowly, hesitantly, conversation began to flow between us. I learned to my surprise that the bookbinder had heard of my name and was, moreover, certain that he had read something by me (for some reason he thought I wrote prose). But that had been so long ago, nearly twenty years.

Truth to tell, I was gratified.

Wind rustled outside. A samovar murmured on the table (such quaint habits). There was a large tree in the bookbinder's garden too, older even than ours, its trunk gnarled. Winter twilight was fading beyond the window, gray tinged by a flaming sunset. Intimations of borderland. He was sitting frozen by my side, an oversized adolescent, the cup of tea full in front of him, the cake beside it untouched. Sitting there hunched, his eyes on the darkening window. Not listening to our talk. Suddenly he pulls out of his pocket a sheet of paper, black with lines of lettering, smooths it out in front of him, slowly writes a single word, and folds it up again.

Our conversation breaks off. The bookbinder and his wife look at him in amazement.

With half a smile I say, "He writes . . ."

They do not understand.

"He is a poet."

"A poet . . . " they whisper.

Just then it began to rain and the sunset kindled the room. He was sitting near the window, his hair aflame.

They stare at me with growing disbelief. And he, pen dropping between his fingers, passes his eyes over us in a pensive glance.

I say to the bookbinder: "He'll publish a book of poetry. You can bind it for him."

The bookbinder is completely at a loss. Am I making fun of him? At last a doubtful smile appears on his face.

"Sure. He'll publish a book. We'll bind it here, together we will."

"For nothing?" I continue the joke.

"For nothing."

I stand up.

"All right, it's a bargain. D'you hear?"

But he hasn't.

(On our way out the bookbinder and his wife pulled me into a corner of the hall and reminded me in a whisper of that part about sickness, or seizures . . . reminded me of their nonresponsibility in such case. I put their minds at rest.)

We went out. The bookbinder could not take us back to the station because the headlights of his old car did not function. We therefore took our leave of him and of his wife and started walking along the road under a soundlessly dripping sky. He was in a state of complete torpor, almost insensible. Dragging his feet over the asphalt. We arrived at the bus stop, stood between the iron railings, the iron roof over us. Housing projects all about, bare rocks, russet soil. A hybrid of town and wasteland. Jerusalem at its saddest, forever destroyed. However much it is built, Jerusalem will always be marked by the memory of its destruction.

I turned to him and the words came out of my mouth pure and clear.

"The bookbinder and his wife are very good people. But you will have to behave yourself."

He kept silent. Someone rode past on a bicycle, caught sight of the boy's face, and turned his head back at once.

Full darkness now. Lights went on in the housing projects. We were standing under the awning, the two of us utterly alone. Suddenly I said: "I had a glimpse of that page and saw—there's a poem there. See, you were able to write by yourself. You did not need me."

He raised his eyes to me, and remained silent.

I drew nearer to him, very near.

"Show me the poem."

"No."

"Why?"

"You'll tear it up . . ."

"No, no, of course I won't . . ."

And I stretched out my hand to take the page. But he shrank back. I meant to use force but he raised his arms to defend himself. This time he would have hit me.

Again someone passed on a bicycle. From the distance came the rumble of the bus.

It had been the last word of his poem.

I did not know.

That was three days ago.

∞

So terrible this season. The windows are covered with mist or frost. I cannot recall such a hard winter before. This lasting leaden gray, day and night, deepening yet toward dawn. Who's that in the mirror? Still I. A furrowed stone. Only the eyes stand out, glittering, amazingly alive.

I am about to leave. I have missed one boat, another is awaiting me. I have only to stuff the last things into the cases, fold the towels, pick up the money, and be off. We have been living here on mattresses a full fortnight now; and the new owner comes and looks at us every day. The man is reaching the end of his patience. He hovers about me in despair, waiting for me to be gone. Yesterday he even threatened me with a lawsuit. He has bought the house with his last pennies. He has his dreams.

Indeed, I must linger no more. I must send the boy to Jerusalem, to the old bookbinder waiting for him by the border. There must be no more lingering. For the boy is forever roaming about these nights. He has stopped writing. Yesterday I waited up for him till after midnight and still he had not come. He returned shortly before the break of dawn. His steps woke me.

The balcony door creaks under my fingers. The floor is wet, strewn with broken leaves and branches, the aftermath of the storm. A cold hopeless sky. A silent drizzle and the first light. This large and so familiar universe silently dripping here before me. The leaves in the tree rustling.

Was there no wish in me to write? Did I not long to write? But what is there left to write about? What more is there to say? I tell you: It is all a fraud. Look, even our poplar is crumbling. Its bark is coming off in strips. The colors of the garden have faded, the stones are gathering moss.

To be driven like a slow arrow to the sky. To sprawl on the cotton clouds, supine, back to earth, face turned to the unchanging blue.

Pensioned-off poet that I am. It is pouring now. Drops splash over me. I dislodge myself and retrace my steps. A bleak silence over the house, the faint wheeze of a snore drifts through it. I go up to his room, nightclothes trailing behind me. My shadow heavy on shut doors.

He is sleeping on a mattress too. His night-light is on the floor by his head. He still cannot fall asleep without his eternal light. The slats of his shutter are slicing constant wafers of dawn light.

I look down silently upon the sleeper at my feet. When I turn to leave the room I suddenly notice some newspaper sheets strewn on the floor by his mattress. Terror grips me. I bend down at once, gather them up. The pages are still damp, the fresh ink comes off on my fingers. I go over to the window, to the faint first light.

A supplement of one of the light, impudent tabloids. And the date—today's, this day about to break. I turn the pages with dead hands. Near the margin of one I discover the poem: crazy, without meter, twisted, lines needlessly cut off, baffling repetitions, arbitrary punctuation.

Suddenly the silence deepens. The sound of breathing has died. He opens his eyes, heavy and red with sleep. His hand fumbles for the spectacles by his mattress. He puts them on, looks at me—me by the window. And a soft, appealing smile, a little sad, lights up his face.

Only now I notice. It is my name plastered across the top of the poem, in battered print. ∽

Interpretive Questions for Discussion

Why is the silent poet unable to love his "borderline" son?

1. Why does the poet insist that it is no reflection on him that his son is feeble-minded? Why does he claim that, "barring a certain ferocity," he and his son have nothing in common? (4)

2. Why do the poet and his wife feel disgraced by and apologetic about her unexpected pregnancy? (5–6)

3. Why do the poet and his daughters see the boy as "a little human being" for the first time after he slashes and buries every photograph of his dead mother? (7)

4. Why is the poet so devastated when the caretaker says of the boy, "Poor kid . . . crazy . . ."? (13)

5. Why does the poet celebrate his son's thirteenth birthday with a party, even though he knows the boy has no friends and he has "passed over" all his other birthdays "in silence"? (15)

6. Looking at his growing, pimple-faced son, why does the poet think that "viewed from a different angle he might fill one with terror"? (18)

7. Why does the period of greatest ease between the poet and his son occur when the boy acts as caretaker and housekeeper for his father? (17–19)

8. Why is the poet so scornful of his son when the youth communicates his impression that the father is unhappy? (30)

9. Why do the poet and his son maintain silence about the boy's mania for poetry? (29)

10. Why does the silent poet decide to retire, sell his house, and travel? Why does he envision escaping to some "remote, decaying port," free of all possessions, even his books? (31, 38)

11. Why is the poet unable to cut loose from his son? Why does the story end with him having missed one boat, living with his son in the empty house, his suitcase still not completely packed?

12. Does the narrator's decision to stop writing poetry render him incapable of being a good parent?

Suggested textual analysis
Pages 5–7: beginning, "He was born late in my life," and ending, "Hiding him was impossible, but we wanted at least to protect him."

Why does the son begin to write poetry?

1. Why is the boy excited and "perfectly content" to be the class monitor? (12)

2. Why does the boy react so passionately to the poem of his father's that is read in class? Why does he throw himself upon the poet and burst into "a kind of savage wail"? (24)

3. Why does the boy lie about what he has done with his father's poetry remnants and notebooks, saying he has thrown them out and sold them? (25)

4. Why does the boy want his father to start writing poetry again?

5. Why does the boy try to tempt his father back to writing poetry by filling the house with flowers and leaving about scraps of the poet's forgotten phrases? (28–29)

6. Why does the son look at his father "in horror," as though he "were beyond hope," when his father mockingly asks him, "Monsieur writes? Yes?" (35)

7. Why does the son take up with a crowd of young writers and intellectuals that the poet refers to as "unkempt, hairy bohemians" and "degenerate creatures"? (33–35)

8. Why are we told that the youth looks at his father with a "soft, appealing smile, a little sad," when he wakes up and sees the poet holding the newspaper that contains his published poem? (43)

9. Why does the son attribute the poem to his father? (43)

10. Are we meant to view the youth's poetry as a feeble imitation of his father's work, or as something genuine in its own right?

Suggested textual analyses
Pages 21–25: beginning, "I was feverish and confined to bed," and ending, "I never imagined it was but the beginning."

Pages 27–31: beginning, "It turned out that those poetry remnants of mine," and ending, "and went into town."

Why does the poet become obsessed with his son when the boy turns his hand to poetry?

1. Why does the narrator become a silent poet? Why does he feel "swept by excitement and despair" after he decides to quit writing poetry? (5)

2. Why does the poet feel compassion when his son has such a powerful response to one of his old poems? (24)

3. Why does the poet "burst out laughing" when his son asks him if he has written any new poems today, and again when he sees the boy's despondent expression at the news that he no longer writes poetry? (25)

4. Why does the poet beat his son when the boy tells him that he has thrown out and sold the poet's old notebooks? Why, just as suddenly, does the poet's anger die? (25)

5. Why does the poet rebel and declare, "These games are over," when the boy begins to plant around the house scraps of lines written in imitation of his father? (29)

6. Why does the poet suggest to his son that the boy could write for him? When his son asks for help, why does the poet experience "a great weariness" and refuse? (30–31)

7. Why does the boy's poetry mania move the poet to seek release from his son by establishing him in some kind of occupation? (32)

8. Why does the poet, who has wished to be free of his son, feel angry and abandoned when the youth takes up with a group of young artists and serves as messenger boy to a literary magazine editor? (35)

9. Why is the poet seized by "inexplicable fury" when his son, who has begun writing poetry, needs help spelling words like "sky" and "independence"? (35–36)

10. Why does the poet readily sign the papers that will transfer responsibility for his son to the Jerusalem bookbinder, and yet experience rage while doing so? (37)

11. Why does terror grip the poet when he notices the newspaper sheets strewn on the floor by his sleeping son and suspects that the boy has published a poem? (43)

12. Are we meant to think that the father will accept his son's offering of love, or that he will reject both the "crazy" poem and its author? (43)

Suggested textual analyses

Pages 3–4: from the beginning of the story to "eyes shut, mouth open, his breathing clear."

Pages 40–43: from "I say to the bookbinder:" to the end of the story.

FOR FURTHER REFLECTION

1. How long are we responsible for our children—for life or until they are adults?

2. Do you blame the poet for wanting to get away from his dependent son before he is too old to travel and enjoy his independence?

3. Does the poet betray himself and his art by maintaining silence rather than enduring the criticism of his fellow poets?

4. Do you pity the silent poet, or do you find him self-absorbed and insensitive?

5. Do you see a relationship between being a parent and being a poet?

GWEN

∼

SOMEWHERE, BELGIUM

Jamaica Kincaid

JAMAICA KINCAID (1949–) was born in
Antigua, in the West Indies, as Elaine Potter
Richardson. When she was sixteen, Kincaid
left Antigua for the United States to continue
her studies and work as a freelance journalist.
In 1976, she became a staff writer for the
New Yorker, which published most of her
early stories. Kincaid's first collection of
short stories, *At the Bottom of the River,*
was published in 1983. Her first novel, *Annie
John,* a series of interconnected stories from
which "Gwen" and "Somewhere, Belgium"
are taken, was published in 1985. Kincaid
has also written a nonfiction study of
Antigua titled *A Small Place,* as well as
the fictional works *Lucy* and *Autobiography
of My Mother.*

Gwen

O N OPENING DAY, I walked to my new school alone. It was the first and last time that such a thing would happen. All around me were other people my age—twelve years—girls and boys, dressed in their school uniforms, marching off to school. They all seemed to know each other, and as they met they would burst into laughter, slapping each other on the shoulder and back, telling each other things that must have made for much happiness. I saw some girls wearing the same uniform as my own, and my heart just longed for them to say something to me, but the most they could do to include me was to smile and nod in my direction as they walked on arm in arm. I could hardly blame them for not paying more attention to me. Everything about me was so new: my uniform was new, my shoes were new, my hat was new, my shoulder ached from the weight of my new books in my new bag; even the road I walked on was new, and I must have put my feet down as if I weren't sure the ground was solid. At school, the yard was filled with more of these girls and their most sure-of-themselves gaits. When I looked at them, they made up a sea. They were walking in and out among the beds of flowers, all across the fields, all across the courtyard, in and out of classrooms. Except for me, no one seemed a stranger to anything or anyone. Hearing the way they greeted each other, I couldn't be sure that they hadn't all come out of the same woman's belly, and at the same time, too. Looking at them, I was suddenly glad that because I had wanted to avoid an argument with my mother I had eaten all my breakfast, for now I surely would have fainted if I had been in any more weakened a condition.

I knew where my classroom was, because my mother and I had kept an appointment at the school a week before. There I met some of my teachers and was shown the ins and outs of everything. When I saw it then, it was nice and orderly and empty and smelled just scrubbed. Now it smelled of girls milling around, fresh ink in inkwells, new books, chalk, and erasers. The girls in my classroom acted even more familiar with each other. I was sure I would never be able to tell them apart just from looking at them, and I was sure that I would never be able to tell them apart from the sound of their voices.

When the school bell rang at half past eight, we formed ourselves into the required pairs and filed into the auditorium for morning prayers and hymn-singing. Our headmistress gave us a little talk, welcoming the new students and welcoming back the old students, saying that she hoped we had all left our bad ways behind us, that we would be good examples for each other and bring greater credit to our school than any of the other groups of girls who had been there before us. My palms were wet, and quite a few times the ground felt as if it were seesawing under my feet, but that didn't stop me from taking in a few things. For instance, the headmistress, Miss Moore. I knew right away that she had come to Antigua from England, for she looked like a prune left out of its jar a long time and she sounded as if she had borrowed her voice from an owl. The way she said, "Now, girls . . ." When she was just standing still there, listening to some of the other activities, her gray eyes going all around the room hoping to see something wrong, her throat would beat up and down as if a fish fresh out of water were caught inside. I wondered if she even smelled like a fish. Once when I didn't wash, my mother had given me a long scolding about it, and she ended by saying that it was the only thing she didn't like about English people: they didn't wash often enough, or wash properly when they finally did. My mother had said, "Have you ever noticed how they smell as if they had been bottled up in a fish?" On either side of Miss Moore stood our other teachers, women and men—mostly women. I recognized Miss George, our music teacher; Miss Nelson, our homeroom teacher; Miss Edward, our history and geography teacher; and Miss Newgate, our algebra and geometry teacher. I had met them the day my mother and I were at school. I did not know who the others were, and I did not worry about it. Since they were teachers, I was sure it wouldn't be long before, because of some misunderstanding, they would be thorns in my side.

We walked back to our classroom the same way we had come, quite orderly and, except for a few whispered exchanges, quite silent. But no sooner were we back in our classroom than the girls were in each other's laps, arms wrapped around necks. After peeping over my shoulder left and right, I sat down in my seat and wondered what would become of me. There were twenty of us in my class, and we were seated at desks arranged five in a row, four rows deep. I was at a desk in the third row, and this made me even more miserable. I hated to be seated so far away from the teacher, because I was sure I would miss something she said. But, even worse, if I was out of my teacher's sight all the time, how could she see my industriousness and quickness at learning things? And, besides, only dunces were seated so far to the rear, and I could not bear to be thought a dunce. I was now staring at the back of a shrubby-haired girl seated in the front row—the seat I most coveted, since it was directly in front of the teacher's desk. At that moment, the girl twisted herself around, stared at me, and said, "You are Annie John? We hear you are very bright." It was a good thing Miss

Nelson walked in right then, for how would it have appeared if I had replied, "Yes, that is completely true"—the very thing that was on the tip of my tongue.

As soon as Miss Nelson walked in, we came to order and stood up stiffly at our desks. She said to us, "Good morning, class," half in a way that someone must have told her was the proper way to speak to us and half in a jocular way, as if we secretly amused her. We replied, "Good morning, Miss," in unison and in a respectful way, at the same time making a barely visible curtsy, also in unison. When she had seated herself at her desk, she said to us, "You may sit now," and we did. She opened the roll book, and as she called out our names each of us answered, "Present, Miss." As she called out our names, she kept her head bent over the book, but when she called out my name and I answered with the customary response she looked up and smiled at me and said, "Welcome, Annie." Everyone, of course, then turned and looked at me. I was sure it was because they could hear the loud racket my heart was making in my chest.

It was the first day of a new term, Miss Nelson said, so we would not be attending to any of our usual subjects; instead, we were to spend the morning in contemplation and reflection and writing something she described as an "autobiographical essay." In the afternoon, we would read aloud to each other our autobiographical essays. (I knew quite well about "autobiography" and "essay," but reflection and contemplation! A day at school spent in such a way! Of course, in most books all the good people were always contemplating and reflecting before they did anything. Perhaps in her mind's eye she could see our futures and, against all prediction, we turned out to be good people.) On hearing this, a huge sigh went up from the girls. Half the sighs were in happiness at the thought of sitting and gazing off into clear space, the other half in unhappiness at the misdeeds that would have to go unaccomplished. I joined the happy half, because I knew it would please Miss Nelson, and, my own selfish interest aside, I liked so much the way she wore her ironed hair and her long-sleeved blouse and box-pleated skirt that I wanted to please her.

The morning was uneventful enough: a girl spilled ink from her inkwell all over her uniform; a girl broke her pen nib and then made a big to-do about replacing it; girls twisted and turned in their seats and pinched each other's bottoms; girls passed notes to each other. All this Miss Nelson must have seen and heard, but she didn't say anything—only kept reading her book: an elaborately illustrated edition of *The Tempest,* as later, passing by her desk, I saw. Midway in the morning, we were told to go out and stretch our legs and breathe some fresh air for a few minutes; when we returned, we were given glasses of cold lemonade and a slice of bun to refresh us.

As soon as the sun stood in the middle of the sky, we were sent home for lunch. The earth may have grown an inch or two larger between the time I had walked to school that morning and the time I went home to lunch, for some girls made a small space for me in their little band. But I couldn't pay much attention to them; my mind was on my new surroundings, my new teacher, what I had written in my nice new notebook with its black-all-mixed-up-with-white cover and smooth lined pages (so glad was I to get rid of my old notebooks, which had on their covers a picture of a wrinkled-up woman wearing a crown on her head and a neckful and armfuls of diamonds and pearls—their pages so coarse, as if they were made of cornmeal). I flew home. I must have eaten my food. I flew back to school. By half past one, we were sitting under a flamboyant tree in a secluded part of our schoolyard, our autobiographical essays in hand. We were about to read aloud what we had written during our morning of contemplation and reflection.

In response to Miss Nelson, each girl stood up and read her composition. One girl told of a much revered and loved aunt who now lived in England and of how much she looked forward to one day moving to England to live with her aunt; one girl told of her brother studying medicine in Canada and the life she imagined he lived there (it seemed quite odd to me); one girl told of the fright she had when she dreamed she was dead, and of the matching fright she had when she woke and found that she wasn't (everyone laughed at this, and Miss Nelson had to call us to order over and over); one girl told of how her oldest sister's best friend's cousin's best friend (it was a real rigmarole) had gone on a Girl Guide jamboree held in Trinidad and met someone who millions of years ago had taken tea with Lady Baden-Powell; one girl told of an excursion she and her father had made to Redonda, and of how they had seen some booby birds tending their chicks. Things went on in that way, all so playful, all so imaginative. I began to wonder about what I had written, for it was the opposite of playful and it was the opposite of imaginative. What I had written was heartfelt, and, except for the very end, it was all too true. The afternoon was wearing itself thin. Would my turn ever come? What should I do, finding myself in a world of new girls, a world in which I was not even near the center?

It was a while before I realized that Miss Nelson was calling on me. My turn at last to read what I had written. I got up and started to read, my voice shaky at first, but since the sound of my own voice had always been a calming potion to me, it wasn't long before I was reading in such a way that, except for the chirp of some birds, the hum of bees looking for flowers, the silvery rush-rush of the wind in the trees, the only sound to be heard was my voice as it rose and fell in sentence after sentence. At the end of my reading, I thought I was imagining the upturned faces on which were looks of adoration, but I was not; I thought I was imagining, too, some eyes brimming over with tears, but again I was not. Miss Nelson said that she would like to borrow what I had written to read for herself, and that it would be placed on the shelf with the books that made up our own class library, so that it would be available to any girl who wanted to read it. This is what I had written:

"When I was a small child, my mother and I used to go down to Rat Island on Sundays right after church, so that I could bathe in the sea. It was at a time when I was thought to have weak kidneys and a bath in the sea had been recommended as a strengthening remedy. Rat Island wasn't a place many people went to anyway, but by climbing down some rocks my mother had found a place that nobody seemed to have ever been. Since this bathing in the sea was a medicine and not a picnic, we had to bathe without wearing swimming costumes. My mother was a superior swimmer. When she plunged into the seawater, it was as if she had always lived there. She would go far out if it was safe to do so, and she could tell just by looking at the way the waves beat if it was safe to do so. She could tell if a shark was nearby, and she had never been stung by a jellyfish. I, on the other hand, could not swim at all. In fact, if I was in water up to my knees I was sure that I was drowning. My mother had tried everything to get me swimming, from using a coaxing method to just throwing me without a word into the water. Nothing worked. The only way I could go into the water was if I was on my mother's back, my arms clasped tightly around her neck, and she would then swim around not too far from the shore. It was only then that I could forget how big the sea was, how far down the bottom could be, and how filled up it was with things that couldn't understand a nice hallo. When we swam around in this way, I would think how much we were like the pictures of sea mammals I had seen, my mother and I, naked in the seawater, my mother sometimes singing to me a song in a French patois I did not yet understand, or sometimes not saying anything at all. I would place my ear against her neck, and it was as if I were listening to a giant shell, for all the sounds around me—the sea, the wind, the birds screeching—would seem as if they came from inside her, the way the sounds of the sea are in a seashell. Afterward, my mother would take me back to the shore, and I would lie there just beyond the farthest reach of a big wave and watch my mother as she swam and dove.

"One day, in the midst of watching my mother swim and dive, I heard a commotion far out at sea. It was three ships going by, and they were filled with people. They must have been celebrating something, for the ships would blow their horns and the people would cheer in response. After they passed out of view, I turned back to look at my mother, but I could not see her. My eyes searched the small area of water where she should have been, but I couldn't find her. I stood up and started to call out her name, but no sound would come out of my throat. A huge black space then opened up in front of me and I fell inside it. I couldn't see what was in front of me and I couldn't hear anything around me. I couldn't think of anything except that my mother was no longer near me. Things went on in this way for I don't know how long. I don't know what, but something drew my eye in one direction. A little bit out of the area in which she usually swam was my mother, just sitting and tracing patterns on a large rock. She wasn't paying any attention to me, for she didn't know that I had missed her. I was glad to see her and started jumping up and down and waving to her. Still she didn't see me, and then I started to cry, for it dawned on me that, with all that water between us and I being unable to swim, my mother could stay there forever and the only way I would be able to wrap my arms around her again was if it pleased her or if I took a boat. I cried until I wore myself out. My tears ran down into my mouth, and it was the first time that I realized tears had a bitter and salty taste. Finally, my mother came ashore. She was, of course, alarmed when she saw my face, for I had let the tears just dry there and they left a stain. When I told her what had happened, she hugged me so close that it was hard to breathe, and she told me that nothing could be farther from the truth—that she would never ever leave me. And though she said it over and over again, and though I felt better, I could not wipe out of my mind the feeling I had had when I couldn't find her.

"The summer just past, I kept having a dream about my mother sitting on the rock. Over and over I would have the dream—only in it my mother never came back, and sometimes my father would join her. When he joined her, they would both sit tracing patterns on the rock, and it must have been amusing, for they would always make each other laugh. At first, I didn't say anything, but when I began to have the dream again and again, I finally told my mother. My mother became instantly distressed; tears came to her eyes, and, taking me in her arms, she told me all the same things she had told me on the day at the sea, and this time the memory of the dark time when I felt I would never see her again did not come back to haunt me."

I didn't exactly tell a lie about the last part. That is just what would have happened in the old days. But actually the past year saw me launched into young-ladyness, and when I told my mother of my dream—my nightmare, really—I was greeted with a turned back and a warning against eating certain kinds of fruit in an unripe state just before going to bed. I placed the old days' version before my classmates because, I thought, I couldn't bear to show my mother in a bad light before people who hardly knew her. But the real truth was that I couldn't bear to have anyone see how deep in disfavor I was with my mother.

☙

As we walked back to the classroom, I in the air, my classmates on the ground, jostling each other to say some words of appreciation and congratulation to me, my head felt funny, as if it had swelled up to the size of, and weighed no more than, a blown-up balloon. Often I had been told by my mother not to feel proud of anything I had done and in the next breath that I couldn't feel enough pride about something I had done. Now I tossed from one to the other: my head bowed down to the ground, my head high up in the air. I looked at these girls surrounding me, my heart filled with just-sprung-up love, and I wished then and there to spend the rest of my life only with them.

As we approached our classroom, I felt a pinch on my arm. It was an affectionate pinch, I could tell. It was the girl who had earlier that day asked me if my name was Annie John. Now she told me that her name was Gweneth Joseph, and reaching into the pocket of her tunic, she brought out a small rock and presented it to me. She had found it, she said, at the foot of a sleeping volcano. The rock was black, and it felt rough in my hands, as if it had been through a lot. I immediately put it to my nose to see what it smelled like. It smelled of lavender, because Gweneth Joseph had kept it wrapped in a handkerchief doused in that scent. It may have been in that moment that we fell in love. Later, we could never agree on when it was. That afternoon, we walked home together, she going a little out of her usual way, and we exchanged likes and dislikes, our jaws dropping and eyes widening when we saw how similar they were. We separated ourselves from the other girls, and they, understanding everything, left us alone. We cut through a tamarind grove, we cut through a cherry-tree grove, we passed down the lane where all the houses had elaborate hedges growing in front, so that nothing was visible but the upstairs windows. When we came to my street, parting was all but unbearable. "Tomorrow," we said, to cheer each other up.

Gwen and I were soon inseparable. If you saw one, you saw the other. For me, each day began as I waited for Gwen to come by and fetch me for school. My heart beat fast as I stood in the front yard of our house waiting to see Gwen as she rounded the bend in our street. The sun, already way up in the sky so early in the morning, shone on her, and the whole street became suddenly empty so that Gwen and everything about her were perfect, as if she were in a picture. Her Panama hat, with the navy blue and gold satin ribbon—our school colors—around the brim, sat lopsided on her head, for her head was small and she never seemed to get the correct-size hat, and it had to be anchored with a piece of elastic running under her chin. The pleats in the tunic of her uniform were in place, as was to be expected. Her cotton socks fit neatly around her ankles, and her shoes shone from just being polished. If a small breeze blew, it would ruffle the ribbons in her short, shrubby hair and the hem of her tunic; if the hem of her tunic was disturbed in that way, I would then be able to see her knees. She had bony knees and they were always ash-colored, as if she had just finished giving them a good scratch or had just finished saying her prayers. The breeze might also blow back the brim of her hat, and since she always walked with her head held down I might then be able to see her face: a small, flattish nose; lips the shape of a saucer broken evenly in two; wide, high cheekbones; ears pinned back close against her head—which was always set in a serious way, as if she were going over in her mind some of the many things we had hit upon that were truly a mystery to us. (Though once I told her that about her face, and she said that really she had only been thinking about me. I didn't look to make sure, but I felt as if my whole skin had become covered with millions of tiny red boils and that shortly I would explode with happiness.) When finally she reached me, she would look up and we would both smile and say softly, "Hi." We'd set off for school side by side, our feet in step, not touching but feeling as if we were joined at the shoulder, hip, and ankle, not to mention heart.

As we walked together, we told each other things we had judged most private and secret: things we had overheard our parents say, dreams we had had the night before, the things we were really afraid of; but especially we told of our love for each other. Except for the ordinary things that naturally came up, I never told her about my changed feeling for my mother. I could see in what high regard Gwen held me, and I couldn't bear for her to see the great thing I had had once and then lost without an explanation. By the time we got to school, our chums often seemed overbearing, with their little comments on the well-pressedness of each other's uniforms, or on the neatness of their schoolbooks, or on how much they approved of the way Miss Nelson was wearing her hair these days. A few other girls were having much the same experience as Gwen and I, and when we heard comments of this kind we would look at each other and roll up our eyes and toss our hands in the air—a way of saying how above such concerns we were. The gesture was an exact copy, of course, of what we had seen our mothers do.

∽

My life in school became just the opposite of my first morning. I went from being ignored, with hardly a glance from anyone, to having girls vie for my friendship, or at least for more than just a passing acquaintanceship. Both my classmates and my teachers noticed how quick I was at learning things. I was soon given responsibility for overseeing the class in the teacher's absence. At first, I was a little taken aback by this, but then I got used to it. I indulged many things, especially if they would end in a laugh or something touching. I would never dillydally with a decision, always making up my mind right away about the thing in front of me. Sometimes, seeing my old frail self in a girl, I would defend her; sometimes, seeing my old frail self in a girl, I would be heartless and cruel. It all went over quite well, and I became very popular.

My so recently much-hated body was now a plus: I excelled at games and was named captain of a volleyball team. As I was favored by my classmates inside and outside the classroom, so was I favored by my teachers—though only inside the classroom, for I had become notorious to them for doing forbidden things. If sometimes I stood away from myself and took a look at who I had become, I couldn't be more surprised at what I saw. But since who I had become earned me the love and devotion of Gwen and the other girls, I was only egged on to find new and better ways to entertain them. I don't know what invisible standard was set, or by whom or exactly when, but eight of us met it, and soon to the other girls we were something to comment on favorably or unfavorably, as the case might be.

It was in a nook of some old tombstones—a place discovered by girls going to our school long before we were born—shaded by trees with trunks so thick it would take four arm's lengths to encircle them, that we would sit and talk about the things we said were on our minds that day. On our minds every day were our breasts and their refusal to budge out of our chests. On hearing somewhere that if a boy rubbed your breasts they would quickly swell up, I passed along this news. Since in the world we occupied and hoped forever to occupy boys were banished, we had to make do with ourselves. What perfection we found in each other, sitting on these tombstones of long-dead people who had been the masters of our ancestors! Nothing in particular really troubled us except for the annoyance of a fly colliding with our lips, sticky from eating fruits; a bee wanting to nestle in our hair; the breeze suddenly blowing too strong. We were sure that the much-talked-about future that everybody was preparing us for would never come, for we had such a powerful feeling against it, and why shouldn't our will prevail this time? Sometimes when we looked at each other, it was all we could do not to cry out with happiness.

My own special happiness was, of course, with Gwen. She would stand in front of me trying to see into my murky black eyes—a way, she said, to tell exactly what I was thinking. After a short while, she would give up, saying, "I can't make out a thing—only my same old face." I would then laugh at her and kiss her on the neck, sending her into a fit of shivers, as if someone had exposed her to a cold draft when she had a fever. Sometimes when she spoke to me, so overcome with feeling would I be that I was no longer able to hear what she said, I could only make out her mouth as it moved up and down. I told her that I wished I had been named Enid, after Enid Blyton, the author of the first books I had discovered on my own and liked. I told her that when I was younger I had been afraid of my mother's dying, but that since I had met Gwen this didn't matter so much. Whenever I spoke of my mother to her, I was always sure to turn the corners of my mouth down, to show my scorn. I said that I could not wait for us to grow up so that we could live in a house of our own. I had already picked out the house. It was a gray one, with many rooms, and it was in the lane where all the houses had high, well-trimmed hedges. With all my plans she agreed, and I am sure that if she had had any plans of her own I would have agreed with them also.

☙

On the morning of the first day I started to menstruate, I felt strange in a new way—hot and cold at the same time, with horrible pains running up and down my legs. My mother, knowing what was the matter, brushed aside my complaints and said that it was all to be expected and I would soon get used to everything. Seeing my gloomy face, she told me in a half-joking way all about her own experience with the first step in coming of age, as she called it, which had happened when she was as old as I was. I pretended that this information made us close—as close as in the old days—but to myself I said, "What a serpent!"

I walked to school with Gwen feeling as I supposed a dog must feel when it has done something wrong and is ashamed of itself and trying to get somewhere quick, where it can lie low. The cloth between my legs grew heavier and heavier with every step I took, and I was sure that everything about me broadcast, "She's menstruating today. She's menstruating today." When Gwen heard what had happened, tears came to her eyes. She had not yet had the wonderful experience, and I could see that she cried for herself. She said that, in sympathy, she would wear a cloth, too.

In class, for the first time in my life, I fainted. Miss Nelson had to revive me, passing her smelling salts, which she had in a beautiful green vial, back and forth under my nose. She then took me to Nurse, who said that it was the fright of all the unexpected pain that had caused me to faint, but I knew that I had fainted after I brought to my mind a clear picture of myself sitting at my desk in my own blood.

At recess, among the tombstones, I of course had to exhibit and demonstrate. None of the others were menstruating yet. I showed everything without the least bit of flourish, since my heart wasn't in it. I wished instead that one of the other girls were in my place and that I were just sitting there in amazement. How nice they all were, though, rallying to my side, offering shoulders on which to lean, laps in which to rest my weary, aching head, and kisses that really did soothe. When I looked at them sitting around me, the church in the distance, beyond that our school, with throngs of girls crossing back and forth in the schoolyard, beyond that the world, how I wished that everything would fall away, so that suddenly we'd be sitting in some different atmosphere, with no future full of ridiculous demands, no need for any sustenance save our love for each other, with no hindrance to any of our desires, which would, of course, be simple desires—nothing, nothing, just sitting on our tombstones forever. But that could never be, as the tolling of the school bell testified.

We walked back to class slowly, as if going to a funeral. Gwen and I vowed to love each other always, but the words had a hollow ring, and when we looked at each other we couldn't sustain the gaze. It had been decided by Miss Nelson and Nurse that I was not to return to school after lunch, with Nurse sending instructions to my mother to keep me in bed for the rest of the day.

When I got home, my mother came toward me, arms outstretched, concern written on her face. My whole mouth filled up with a bitter taste, for I could not understand how she could be so beautiful even though I no longer loved her. ◡

Somewhere, Belgium

IN THE YEAR I turned fifteen, I felt more unhappy than I had ever imagined anyone could be. It wasn't the unhappiness of wanting a new dress, or the unhappiness of wanting to go to cinema on a Sunday afternoon and not being allowed to do so, or the unhappiness of being unable to solve some mystery in geometry, or the unhappiness at causing my dearest friend, Gwen, some pain. My unhappiness was something deep inside me, and when I closed my eyes I could even see it. It sat somewhere—maybe in my belly, maybe in my heart; I could not exactly tell—and it took the shape of a small black ball, all wrapped up in cobwebs. I would look at it and look at it until I had burned the cobwebs away, and then I would see that the ball was no bigger than a thimble, even though it weighed worlds. At that moment, just when I saw its size and felt its weight, I was beyond feeling sorry for myself, which is to say I was beyond tears. I could only just sit and look at myself, feeling like the oldest person who had ever lived and who had not learned a single thing. After I had sat in this way for a while, to distract myself I would count my toes; always it came out the same—I had ten of them.

If I had been asked, I would not have been able to say exactly how it was that I got that way. It must have come on me like mist: first, I was in just a little mist and could still see everything around me, though not so clearly; then I was completely covered up and could not see even my own hand stretched out in front of me. I tried to imagine that I was like a girl in one of the books I had read—a girl who had suffered much at the hands of a cruel stepparent, or a girl who suddenly found herself without any parents at all. When reading about such a girl, I would heap even more suffering on her if I felt the author hadn't gone far enough. In the end, of course, everything was resolved happily for the girl, and she and a companion would sail off to Zanzibar or some other very distant place, where, since they could do as they pleased, they were forever happy. But I was not in a book. I was always just sitting there with the thimble that weighed worlds fastened deep inside me, the sun beating down on me. Everything I used to care about had turned sour. I could start with the sight of the flamboyant trees in bloom, the red of the flowers causing the street on which I lived to seem on fire at sunset; seeing this sight, I would imagine myself incapable of coming to harm if I were just to walk through this inferno. I could end with my mother and me; we were now a sight to see.

We both noticed that now if she said that something I did reminded her of her own self at my age, I would try to do it a different way, or, failing that, do it in a way that she could not stomach. She returned the blow by admiring and praising everything that she suspected had special meaning for me. I became secretive, and she said that I was in practice for becoming a liar and a thief—the only kinds of people who had secrets. My mother and I each soon grew two faces: one for my father and the rest of the world, and one for us when we found ourselves alone with each other. For my father and the world, we were politeness and kindness and love and laughter. I saw her with my old eyes, my eyes as a child, and she saw me with hers of that time. There was my mother scrubbing my back as in the old days, examining my body from limb to limb, making sure nothing unusual was taking place; there was my mother making me my favorite dessert, a blancmange—a reward for excelling at something that met her approval; there was my mother concerned about a small sniffle, wondering if soon it would develop into something major and then she would have to make me a poultice of ground camphor and eucalyptus leaves for my chest. And there I was also, letting the singsong of her voice, as it expressed love and concern, calm me into a lull; there I was fondling the strands of her thick black hair as she unraveled her braids for a daily brushing, burying my face in it and inhaling deeply, for it smelled of rose oil.

As we were playing out these scenes from the old days, the house would swell with the sound of my father's voice telling one story after another of his days as a famous batsman with a cricket team, and of what he did on this island and the next as he toured the Windward and the Leeward Islands with his teammates. In front of my mother's friends also, we put on our good faces. I was obedient and nice, and she asked nothing more than that I show the good manners she had taught me. Sometimes on Sundays as we walked back from church, perhaps touched by the sermon we had just heard, we would link arms as we strolled home, step in step with each other.

But no sooner were we alone, behind the fence, behind the closed door, than everything darkened. How to account for it I could not say. Something I could not name just came over us, and suddenly I had never loved anyone so or hated anyone so. But to say hate—what did I mean by that? Before, if I hated someone I simply wished the person dead. But I couldn't wish my mother dead. If my mother died, what would become of me? I couldn't imagine my life without her. Worse than that, if my mother died I would have to die, too, and even less than I could imagine my mother dead could I imagine myself dead.

I started to have a dream. In my dream, I walked down a smooth, unpaved road. The road was lined on either side with palm trees whose leaves spread out so wide that they met and tangled up with each other and the whole road was shaded from the sun, which was always shining. When I started to walk down the road, my steps were quick and light, and as I walked these words would go around in my head: "My mother would kill me if she got the chance. I would kill my mother if I had the courage." At the beginning of my walk, as I chanted the words my voice had a happy note, as if the quickness and lightness of my feet signaled to me that I would never give her the chance. But as the road went on, things changed. I would say the same words, but slower and slower and in a sad way; my feet and the rest of my body became heavy. It was as if it had dawned on me that I would never have the courage with which to kill my mother, and then, since I lacked the courage the chance would pass to her. I did not understand how it became so, but just the same it did. I had been taught by my mother to take my dreams seriously. My dreams were not unreal representations of something real; my dreams were a part of, and the same as, my real life. When I first had this dream, I became quite frightened of my mother, and I was so ashamed of it that I couldn't bring myself to look directly at her. But after I had had the dream again and again, it became like a second view to me, and I would hold up little incidents against it to see if this was her chance or that was my courage.

∞

At school, I had had a great change. I was no longer in the same class with Gwen; I was now in a class with girls two or three years older than I was. That was a shock. These girls didn't offer the camaraderie of my friends in the second form. They didn't have the give-and-take, the friendly pull-and-shove. They were constantly in strict competition for good marks and our teachers' affection, and among them insults ruled the day. And how vain they were! Constantly they smoothed down their hair, making sure every strand was in place; some carried mirrors in their schoolbags, and they would hold them at an angle to see if the pleats in the backs of their uniforms were in place. They actually practiced walking with their hips swinging from side to side. They were always sticking out their bosoms, and, what was worse, they actually did have bosoms to stick out. Before I got to see these girls close up—when I was just observing them as they walked to and fro, going about their business—I envied the way the air seemed to part for them, freeing itself of any obstacle so that they wouldn't have to make an effort. Now I could see that the air just parted itself quickly so that it wouldn't have to bear their company for long. For what a dull bunch they were! They had no different ideas of how to be in the world; they certainly didn't think that the world was a strange place to be caught living in.

I was at first slowed down in my usual climb to the top by the new subjects put before me, but I soon mastered them, and only one other girl was my match. Sometimes we tied for first place, sometimes she was first and I second, and sometimes it was the other way around. I tried to get to know her, feeling that we had this much in common, but she was so dull a person, completely unable to hold so much as a simple conversation, and, to boot, smelled so of old rubber and blue ink, that I made myself unable to remember her name. I could see the kind of grown-up person she would be—just the kind who would take one look at me and put every effort into making my life a hardship. Already her mouth was turned down permanently at the corners, as if to show that she had been born realizing that nobody else behaved properly, and as if also she had been born knowing that everything in life was a disappointment and her face was all set to meet it.

Gwen and I walked home from school in the usual way and did the usual things, but just the sight of her was no longer a thrill to me, though I did my best not to let her know. It was as if I had grown a new skin over the old skin and the new skin had a completely different set of nerve endings. But what could I say to poor Gwen? How to explain to her about the thimble that weighed worlds, and the dark cloud that was like an envelope in which my mother and I were sealed? If I said to Gwen, "Does your mother always watch you out of the corner of her eye?" her reply was most likely to be "My mother has a knack for keeping her eye on everything at the same time." And if I said, "I don't mean in that way, I mean—." But what would have been the use of going on? We no longer lived on the same plane. Sometimes, just hearing her voice as she ran on and on, bringing me up to date on the doings of my old group, would put me in such a state that I felt I would explode; and then I remembered that it was the same voice that used to be, for me, some sort of music. How small she now looked in my eyes: a bundle of who said what and who did what.

One day when we were walking home, taking the lane with the big houses hidden behind the high hedges, Gwen said to me that her brother Rowan had mentioned how much he liked the way I had conducted myself when I was asked to read the lesson in church one Sunday. She then launched into a long speech about him, and I did what was fast becoming a habit when we were together: I started to daydream. My most frequent daydream now involved scenes of me living alone in Belgium, a place I had picked when I read in one of my books that Charlotte Brontë, the author of my favorite novel, *Jane Eyre,* had spent a year or so there. I had also picked it because I imagined that it would be a place my mother would find difficult to travel to and so would have to write me letters addressed in this way:

> To: *Miss Annie Victoria John*
> *Somewhere,*
> *Belgium*

I was walking down a street in Belgium, wearing a skirt that came down to my ankles and carrying a bag filled with books that at last I could understand, when suddenly I heard these words come out of Gwen's mouth: "I think it would be so nice if you married Rowan. Then, you see, that way we could be together always."

I was brought back to the present, and I stopped and stood still for a moment; then my mouth fell open and my whole self started to tremble. All this was in disbelief, of course, but, to show how far apart we were, she thought that my mouth fell open and my whole self trembled in complete joy at what she had said to me. And when I said, "What did you just say?" she said, "Oh, I knew you would like the idea." I felt so alone; the last person left on earth couldn't feel more alone than I. I looked at Gwen. Could this really be Gwen? It was Gwen. The same person I had always known. Everything was in place. But at the same time something terrible had happened, and I couldn't tell what it was.

It was then that I began avoiding Gwen and our daily walks home. I tried not to do it so much that she would notice, but about every three or four days I would say that being in my new class was so demanding and, what with one thing and another, I had things to clear up here and there. I would walk her to the school gate, where we would kiss goodbye, and then, after some proper time had passed, I would leave school. One afternoon, I took another way home, a way that brought me through Market Street. Market Street was where all the stores were, and I passed by slowly, staring into the shop windows, though I wasn't at all interested in the merchandise on display. What I was really looking at was my own reflection in the glass, though it was a while before I knew that. I saw myself just hanging there among bolts of cloth, among Sunday hats and shoes, among men's and women's undergarments, among pots and pans, among brooms and household soap, among notebooks and pens and ink, among medicines for curing headache and medicines for curing colds. I saw myself among all these things, but I didn't know that it was I, for I had got so strange. My whole head was so big, and my eyes, which were big, too, sat in my big head wide open, as if I had just had a sudden fright. My skin was black in a way I had not noticed before, as if someone had thrown a lot of soot out of a window just when I was passing by and it had all fallen on me. On my forehead, on my cheeks, were little bumps, each with a perfect, round white point. My plaits stuck out in every direction from under my hat; my long, thin neck stuck out from the blouse of my uniform. Altogether, I looked old and miserable. Not long before, I had seen a picture of a painting entitled *The Young Lucifer*. It showed Satan just recently cast out of heaven for all his bad deeds, and he was standing on a black rock all alone and naked. Everything around him was charred and black, as if a great fire had just roared through. His skin was coarse, and so were all his features. His hair was made up of live snakes, and they were in a position to strike. Satan was wearing a smile, but it was one of those smiles that you could see through, one of those smiles that make you know the person is just putting up a good front. At heart, you could see, he was really lonely and miserable at the way things had turned out. I was standing there surprised at this change in myself, when all this came to mind, and suddenly I felt so sorry for myself that I was about to sit down on the sidewalk and weep, already tasting the salty bitterness of my tears.

I was about to do this when I noticed four boys standing across the street from me; they were looking at me and bowing as they said, in an exaggerated tone of voice, pretending to be grown-up gentlemen living in Victorian times, "Hallo, Madame. How are you this afternoon?" and "What a pleasant thing, our running into each other like this," and "We meet again after all this time," and "Ah, the sun, it shines and shines only on you." The words were no sooner out of their mouths than they would bend over laughing. Even though nothing like this had ever happened to me before, I knew instantly that it was malicious and that I had done nothing to deserve it other than standing there all alone. They were older than I, and from their uniforms I could tell that they were students of the boys' branch of my own school. I looked at their faces. I didn't recognize the first, I didn't recognize the second, I didn't recognize the third, but I knew the face of the fourth one; it was a face from my ancient history. A long time ago, when we were little children, our mothers were best friends, and he and I used to play together. His name was Mineu, and I felt pleased that he, a boy older than I by three years, would play with me. Of course, in all the games we played I was always given the lesser part. If we played knight and dragon, I was the dragon; if we played discovering Africa, he discovered Africa; he was also the leader of the savage tribes that tried to get in the way of the discovery, and I played his servant, and a not very bright servant at that; if we played prodigal son, he was the prodigal son and the prodigal son's father and the jealous brother, while I played a person who fetched things.

Once, in a game we were playing, something terrible happened. A man had recently killed his girlfriend and a man who was his best friend when he found them drinking together in a bar. Their blood splattered all over him. The cutlass he had used to kill them in hand, he walked the mile or so to the police station with the other customers of the bar and some people they picked up along the way. The murder of these two people immediately became a big scandal, and the most popular calypso song that year was all about it. It became a big scandal because the murderer was from an old, well-off, respected family, and everybody wondered if he would be hanged, which was the penalty for murder; also it became a scandal because everyone had known the woman and all had predicted that she would come to a bad end. Everything about this soon became a spectacle. During the funerals of the murdered man and woman, people lined the streets and followed the hearses from the church to the cemetery. During the trial of the murderer, the courtroom was always packed. When the judge sentenced the man to be hanged, the whole courtroom gasped in shock. On the morning that he was hanged, people gathered outside the jail and waited until the jail's church bell rang, showing that the hanging was completed. Mineu and I had overheard our parents talk so much about this event that it wasn't long before he made up a game about it. As usual, Mineu played all the big parts. He played the murdered man and the murderer, going back and forth; the girlfriend we left silent. When the case got to court, Mineu played judge, jury, prosecutor, and condemned man, sitting in the condemned man's box. Nothing was funnier than seeing him, using some old rags as a wig for his part of the judge, pass sentence on himself; nothing was funnier than seeing him, as the drunken hangman, hang himself. And after he was hanged, I, as his mother, came and wept over the body as it lay on the ground. Then we would get up and start the whole thing over again. No sooner had we completed the episode than we were back at the bar, with Mineu quarreling with himself and his girlfriend and then putting an end to everything with a few quick strokes. We always tried to make every detail as close to the real thing as we imagined it, and so we had gone to the trouble of finding old furniture to make a desk for the judge and a place for the jury to sit, and we set out some stones facing the judge to represent both where the spectators might sit and the spectators themselves. When it came to the hanging, we wanted that to be real, too, so Mineu had found a piece of rope and tied it to the top bar of the gate to his yard, and then he would make a noose and put his head in it. When the noose was around his neck, he would grab the rope from above and then swing on it back and forth to show that he was hanged and already dead. All of our playing together came to an end when something bad almost happened. We were playing in the usual way when we came to the part of the noose around the neck. When he lifted himself off the ground, the noose tightened. When he let go of the rope to loosen the noose with his hands, that only made matters worse, and the noose tightened even more. His mouth opened as he tried to get breath, and then his tongue began to come out of his mouth. His body, hanging from the gate, began to swing back and forth, and as it did it banged against the gate, and it made a sound as if he were swinging on the gate—the very thing we were always being told not to do. As all this happened, I just stood there and stared. I must have known that I should go and call for help, but I was unable to move. *Slam, slam* went the gate, and soon his mother began to call out, "Children, leave the gate alone." Then, hearing the gate continue to slam, she came out to us in a fury, because we were not obeying her, and she was just about to shout at us when she saw her child swinging from the gate by his neck. She screamed and rushed over to him, calling out to a neighbor, who came immediately with a cutlass and cut the rope from around Mineu's neck. When his mother came and started to scream, only then could I scream, too, and I ran over to him with her, and we both cried over him as he fell to the ground. Much was said about my not calling for help, and everybody wondered what would have happened if his mother hadn't been nearby. I didn't know what to make of my own behavior, and I could not explain myself, as everybody kept asking me to do. I could see that even my mother was ashamed of the way I had behaved.

It was this that I remembered as I saw Mineu's face across the street, and so I walked over and said in my best, most polite young-lady voice, "Hallo, Mineu. I am so glad to see you. Don't you remember me?" It was true that I was glad to see him. For just remembering all the things that he and I used to do reminded me of how happy I had been and how much my mother and everyone else adored me and how, when looking at me, people used to say, "What a beautiful child!"

At first, he just looked at me. Then he said, "Oh, yes. Annie. Annie John. I remember you. I had heard you were a big girl now." As he said this, he shook my outstretched hand. His friends stood off to one side, a little bit apart from us. They stood in that ridiculous way of boys: one leg crossing the other, hands jammed deep into pockets, eyes looking you up and down. They were whispering things to each other, and their shoulders were heaving with amusement—at me, I could only suppose. I thought that since he was someone I knew, he couldn't really be like them, but as we stood, more or less speechless, in front of each other, I saw him glancing at them out of the corner of his eye, smiling in a knowing way, and then looking back straight at me, a serious look on his face.

Feeling ashamed, for I could tell that they were making fun of me, I said to him, "Well, goodbye then," and I offered him my hand again.

He and his friends walked off, their backs shaking with laughter—at me, no doubt. As I watched them, I wished that right there I could turn them into cinder blocks, so that one moment if you were walking behind them you were walking behind four boys and the next moment you had to be careful not to stumble over some cinder blocks. Feeling that in this whole incident Mineu had been cruel made me remember something. It was the last time that we had played together. In a game we were making up on the spot, I took off all my clothes and he led me to a spot under a tree, where I was to sit until he told me what to do next. It wasn't long before I realized that the spot he had picked out was a red ants' nest. Soon the angry ants were all over me, stinging me in my private parts, and as I cried and scratched, trying to get the ants off me, he fell down on the ground laughing, his feet kicking the air with happiness. His mother refused to admit that he had done something wrong, and my mother never spoke to her again.

☙

I walked home, cutting through the churchyard of the Methodist church (my own church). Except for two lizards chasing each other across my path, I wasn't aware of anything on the outside. Inside, however, the thimble that weighed worlds spun around and around; as it spun, it bumped up against my heart, my chest, my stomach, and whatever it touched felt as if I had been scorched there. I thought that I had better get home quickly, for I began to feel alternately too big and too small. First, I grew so big that I took up the whole street; then I grew so small that nobody could see me—not even if I cried out.

I walked into our yard, and I could see my mother standing in the kitchen, her back toward me, bent over a bowl in which she was putting some green figs, their skins removed. I walked up to her and I said, "Good afternoon, Mamie. I have just come home from school."

80

My mother turned to face me. We looked at each other, and I could see the frightening black thing leave her to meet the frightening black thing that had left me. They met in the middle and embraced. What will it be now, I asked myself. To me she said, "You are late. It would please me to hear an excuse from you." She was using that tone of voice: it was as if I were not only a stranger but a stranger that she did not wish to know.

Trying to match her tone of voice but coming nowhere near success, I said something about being kept late for extra studies. I then went on to say that my teachers believed that if I studied hard enough, by my sixteenth birthday I might be able to take final exams and so be able to leave school.

As if she knew exactly that I would come up with some such story, she said, "Perhaps if I ask again this time I will get a straight answer." I was about to make a feeble effort at protest, but then, in a rush, she said that she had been standing inside a store that afternoon, buying some buttons for a Sunday dress for me, when, on looking up, she observed me making a spectacle of myself in front of four boys. She went on to say that, after all the years she had spent drumming into me the proper way to conduct myself when speaking to young men, it had pained her to see me behave in the manner of a slut (only she used the French-patois word for it) in the street and that just to see me had caused her to feel shame.

The word "slut" (in patois) was repeated over and over, until suddenly I felt as if I were drowning in a well but instead of the well being filled with water it was filled with the word "slut," and it was pouring in through my eyes, my ears, my nostrils, my mouth. As if to save myself, I turned to her and said, "Well, like father like son, like mother like daughter."

At that, everything stopped. The whole earth fell silent. The two black things joined together in the middle of the room separated, hers going to her, mine coming back to me. I looked at my mother. She seemed tired and old and broken. Seeing that, I felt happy and sad at the same time. I soon decided that happy was better, and I was just about to enjoy this feeling when she said, "Until this moment, in my whole life I knew without a doubt that, without any exception, I loved you best," and then she turned her back and started again to prepare the green figs for cooking.

I looked at my mother—at her turned back this time—and she wasn't tired and old and broken at all. She wore her hair pinned up in the same beautiful way, exposing the nape of her beautiful neck; her bent-over back looked strong and soft at the same time, and I wanted to go and rest my whole body on it the way I used to; her long skirt covered her beautiful, strong legs, and she wore shoes that exposed beautiful heels. It was I who was tired and old and broken, and as I looked at my mother, full of vigor, young and whole, I wanted to go over and put my arms around her and beg forgiveness for the thing I had just said and to explain that I didn't really mean it. But I couldn't move, and when I looked down it was as if the ground had opened up between us, making a deep and wide split. On one side of this split stood my mother, bent over my dinner cooking in a pot; on the other side stood I, in my arms carrying my schoolbooks and inside carrying the thimble that weighed worlds.

I went to my room to take off my school uniform, but I could only sit on my bed and wonder what would become of me now. As I sat, I looked at the things surrounding me. There was my washstand, made for me by my father from pitch pine, with its enamel basin on top and matching urn filled with water underneath; there was my bureau, made for me by my father from pitch pine, and in it were my clothes; there was a shelf made for me by my father from pitch pine on which I kept my books; the very bed I sat on was made for me by my father from pitch pine; there was a little desk and chair to match at which I sat and read or did my homework, both made for me by my father from pitch pine. Each time my father had bought the wood for the furniture, he had taken me to the lumber yard with him, and I saw how he examined every piece of wood carefully before he accepted it for purchase. He would hold it first to his nostrils, then to my own, and he would say, "Nothing like a nice piece

of pine, except perhaps a nice piece of mahogany." Then I was
not allowed to see the furniture in any stage until it was in its
place in my room. It would be a surprise then for me to see it,
and I would say to my father, "I see I have a new chair," and he
would say, "I see you have a new chair," and then we would
embrace, I kissing him on the cheek and he kissing me on the
forehead. It used to be that when my father wanted to kiss me
he would have to bend down to reach my forehead. Now, in the
last year, I had grown so much that it was I who had to bend
down so that my father could reach my forehead. My mother
was taller than my father. Now I, too, was taller than my father.
I was, in fact, as tall as my mother. When my mother and I spoke
to each other, we looked at each other eye to eye. Eye to eye. It
was the first time such a thing had come to me: my mother and
I were eye to eye. For a moment, I was happy at the thought, but
then I could see: what did such a thing matter? She was my
mother, Annie; I was her daughter, Annie; and that was why I
was called by my mother and father Little Miss.

Sitting on my bed and thinking in this way, I swung my feet
back and forth, and it was a while before I realized that when
they swung back my feet would hit up against the trunk stored
under my bed. It was the trunk that my mother had bought
when she was sixteen years old—a year older than I was now—
and in which she had packed all her things and left not only her
parents' house in Dominica but Dominica itself for Antigua.
Her father and she had had a big quarrel over whether she
would live alone, as she wished, or would continue to live in her
parents' house, as her father wished. Her mother, who had
stopped speaking to her father a long time before, though they
continued to live in the same house, didn't say anything one way
or the other. My mother and her father had had a big quarrel,
and though my mother had never told me in detail the whole
story, I had pieced it together from things I had overheard, just
putting two and two together in my usual way. Inside this trunk
now were the things, all of them, that had been a part of my life
at every stage, and if someone had come upon it without having

an inkling of what my life had really been like, they would have got a pretty good idea. As my heels bumped up against the trunk, my heart just broke, and I cried and cried. At that moment, I missed my mother more than I had ever imagined possible and wanted only to live somewhere quiet and beautiful with her alone, but also at that moment I wanted only to see her lying dead, all withered and in a coffin at my feet.

The moment soon passed, and I got up from my bed to change my clothes and carry out my afternoon chores. My mother and I avoided each other, and it wasn't until over our supper of the green figs, cooked with fish in coconut milk, that we looked at each other again. We did our best to keep up appearances, for my father's sake, but our two black things got the better of us, and even though we didn't say anything noticeable it was clear that something was amiss. Perhaps to cheer us up, my father said that he would finally make for my mother the set of furniture she had been asking him to make for a very long time now. In fact, the set of furniture had been a bone of contention between them. That brought a halfhearted, polite smile to my mother's face. Then, turning to me, my father asked what he could make for me.

It came into my mind without thinking. "A trunk," I said.

"But you have a trunk already. You have your mother's trunk," he said to me.

"Yes, but I want my own trunk," I said back.

"Very well. A trunk is your request, a trunk you will have," he said.

Out of the corner of one eye, I could see my mother. Out of the corner of the other eye, I could see her shadow on the wall, cast there by the lamplight. It was a big and solid shadow, and it looked so much like my mother that I became frightened. For I could not be sure whether for the rest of my life I would be able to tell when it was really my mother and when it was really her shadow standing between me and the rest of the world. ∽

Interpretive Questions for Discussion

Why does Annie feel that she cannot tell even Gwen her true feelings about her mother?

1. Why does Annie choose as the topic of her autobiographical essay the time she was separated from her mother by an expanse of sea? Why must Annie ride on her mother's back, clinging to her neck, in order to forget her fear of the sea? (59)

2. Why does Annie begin dreaming about this long-ago day at the sea during the year she is "launched into young-ladyness"? (60–61)

3. Why do Annie and Gwen fall in love with each other and become inseparable?

4. Why is Annie loved at school but not at home? Why does Annie's essay make her popular with the other girls?

5. Why does Annie imagine that Gwen's regard for her would lessen if she knew about the change in feeling between herself and her mother—"the great thing I had had once and then lost without an explanation"? (63)

6. Why does Annie seemingly develop a double life, doing forbidden things outside the classroom to earn the love of Gwen and the other girls? (64)

7. Why does Gwen try, and fail, to know exactly what Annie is thinking? (65)

8. Why does her friendship with Gwen enable Annie to overcome her fear of her mother's death? (65)

9. Why does Annie's love for Gwen begin to wane when Annie begins to menstruate? (67) Why does Gwen eventually appear to Annie to be as conventional and "small" as the older girls in her class? (73–74)

10. Why is Annie so overcome by Gwen's suggestion that she marry her brother Rowan that she starts avoiding and deceiving Gwen? Why does Annie feel that with Gwen's innocent suggestion "something terrible had happened" that she couldn't identify? (74–75)

Suggested textual analysis
Pages 57–61: beginning, "In response to Miss Nelson," and ending, "how deep in disfavor I was with my mother."

Why can't Annie reconcile her feelings of love and hate for her mother?

1. Why does Annie think to herself "What a serpent!" when her mother confides her own first experience with menstruation? Why does Annie only pretend that this confidence brings them as close together "as in the old days"? (65–66)

2. When she comes home from school on the day of her first period, why can't Annie accept the love her mother offers? Why does Annie bitterly wonder how her mother could be so beautiful even though Annie no longer loves her? (67)

3. Why does Annie sense that she feels both love and hate for her mother, but then think that she couldn't imagine her life without her? Why does Annie say that if her mother died, she would have to die, too? (71)

4. Why does Annie dream of walking happily down a road, thinking, "My mother would kill me if she got the chance. I would kill my mother if I had the courage"? (72)

5. Why does Annie come to see little incidents in her life as a test of whether her mother has a chance to kill her, or whether she has the courage to kill her mother? (72)

6. Why does Annie experience arguments with her mother as two frightening black things emerging from them and embracing in the middle of the room? (80, 81)

7. Why does Annie's mother say that Annie was behaving like a slut when she spoke to Mineu? (81) Whose version of the story are we meant to believe—Annie's or her mother's?

8. Why does her mother appear to Annie as "tired and old and broken" when Annie feels she has won the argument, and as strong, soft, and beautiful when Annie feels that her mother has gained the upper hand? (81–82)

9. Why is Annie unable to ask her mother to forgive her, even though she longs to feel close to her mother again? (82)

10. Does Annie's ambivalence toward her mother stem from the fact that her mother is beautiful while Annie, in her difficult puberty, is not?

Suggested textual analyses

Pages 69–72: beginning, "In the year I turned fifteen," and ending, "if this was her chance or that was my courage."

Pages 74–76: beginning, "One day when we were walking home," and ending, "the salty bitterness of my tears."

Are Annie's feelings of sadness and confusion a normal adolescent response to her troubled relationship with her mother, or are they signs of emotional illness?

1. Why does Annie envision the profound sadness she feels when she is fifteen as a small, heavy black ball, wrapped up in cobwebs? Why does she imagine that she can burn away the cobwebs, but not dispel the feeling of helpless despair? (69)

2. Why can't Annie and her mother merge the two faces they have—the one for the world and the one they put on when alone with each other? Why can they pretend to be kind, polite, loving, and joyful but not sincerely feel it? (70–71)

3. Why does Annie make her dreams a part of and the same as her real life, rather than seeing them as unreal representations of something real? (71–72)

4. Why does Annie dream about living in "Somewhere, Belgium," a place her mother would have difficulty traveling to? (74)

5. Why does the author have Annie stare through the store windows but really see only her own reflection? Why does looking at her reflection make Annie empathize with the young Lucifer, just cast out of heaven, who smiles to hide his true feelings of loneliness and misery? (75–76)

6. Are we meant to interpret Annie's not calling for help when Mineu was being strangled as a sign of her lack of connection with people, or an example of how she is always misunderstood? (78–79)

7. While rushing home after her encounter with Mineu and his friends, why does Annie alternate between feeling that she has grown too big and then too small? (80)

8. Why does the argument about Annie's "sluttish" behavior end when Annie says to her mother, "like mother like daughter"? Why does Annie feel both happy and sad at this ending, but then decide to let her happiness win out? (81)

9. Why does Annie ask her father for her own trunk to replace her mother's, which was being used for Annie's things? (84)

10. Why does Annie begin to fear that, for the rest of her life, she might not be able to tell when it was her mother and when it was her mother's shadow that stood between her and the rest of the world? (84)

Suggested textual analysis
Pages 83–84: from "Sitting on my bed," to the end of the selection.

FOR FURTHER REFLECTION

1. Should Annie's mother have sympathized more with the emotional suffering of her daughter, or did Annie make it impossible for her to do so?

2. Is Annie self-centered and arrogant or honest and artless?

3. Did Annie's mother love her daughter too little or too much?

4. Does an "only child" have a harder time breaking away from the focused attention of a parent than do children who have siblings?

5. Is it inevitable that an "ugly duckling" daughter will act out against her beautiful mother?

6. When an adolescence is as difficult as Annie's, is it best for parents and children to live apart for a while?

7. Is the mother-daughter relationship parallel to that of father and son? Does each face the same difficulties and tensions?

8. How can parents deal with the kind of resentment Annie feels toward her mother?

Iphigeneia at Aulis

Euripides

EURIPIDES (484?–406 B.C.) was born in
Phyla, a village north of the ancient city of
Athens, but lived most of his life in Athens.
The youngest of the three great Greek
tragedians, following Aeschylus and
Sophocles, Euripides authored more than
ninety plays, of which fewer than twenty
survive. In the fifty years of his dramatic
career, he won only a few first prizes in the
competition held at the annual spring festival
of Dionysus in Athens. This small number
of awards was perhaps due to his penchant
for raising questions that his audiences found
disturbing. Two years before his death,
Euripides left Athens to live in Macedonia—
a move motivated, it is thought, by his
disappointment at the reception of his plays
and perhaps also by his feelings of dismay
at the ruinous effects of the Peloponnesian
War, then in its twenty-third year. It was
during this period of voluntary exile that
Euripides wrote his last two plays,
Iphigeneia at Aulis and *The Bacchae.*

CHARACTERS

AGAMEMNON	King of Mycenae, leader of the Greek expedition against Troy
OLD MAN	Clytemnestra's slave, attendant on Agamemnon
CHORUS	of young women of Chalkis
MENELAOS	brother of Agamemnon, husband of Helen of Troy
FIRST MESSENGER	leader of Clytemnestra's escort
ATTENDANTS	of Clytemnestra
CLYTEMNESTRA	Queen of Mycenae
IPHIGENEIA	daughter of Agamemnon and Clytemnestra
ORESTES	infant son of Agamemnon and Clytemnestra
ACHILLES	hero-to-be of the Trojan War
SECOND MESSENGER	

SCENE: *In front of Agamemnon's tent, in the camp of the Greek armies by the bay at Aulis, where the ships are waiting. It is some time before dawn. As the light rises it will be perceived that the tent has a main entrance flanked by two side doors.* AGAMEMNON *enters through the main door, a waxed tablet in his hand. He paces up and down before the tent in great indecision, then turns and calls in at the main door.*

AGAMEMNON: Come here, old man. In front of my tent.

OLD MAN (*inside*): I'm coming. Is there something new,
    King Agamemnon?

AGAMEMNON: Be quick about it!

OLD MAN (*entering*): I am quick. There's no sleep in me.
    My eyes won't stay shut now they're old.

AGAMEMNON: What star is that, what time
    crossing heaven?

OLD MAN: Sirius, pursuing the seven Pleiades,
    still traveling high at this hour.

AGAMEMNON: No bird-sound, no murmur from the sea.
    The winds are silent along these
    straits of Euripos.

OLD MAN: Then why are you up
    pacing outside your tent, King Agamemnon?

There's not a voice stirring yet in Aulis.
The watch is quiet
up on the walls.
Might we not go in?

AGAMEMNON: I envy you, old man. I envy any man
whose life passes quietly, unnoticed by fame.
I do not envy those in authority.

OLD MAN: But it is they who have the good of life.

AGAMEMNON: You call that good? It's a trap. Great honors
taste sweet
but they come bringing pain.
Something goes wrong
between a man and the gods
and his whole life is overturned.
At other times the notions of men, all
different and all insatiable,
grate it away by themselves.

OLD MAN: I don't like it, hearing a king
talk that way. Atreus did not
sire you, Agamemnon, into a world
of pure happiness. You must expect
to suffer as well as rejoice,
since you're a man.
And the gods will see to that, whether
you like it or not.
But you've lit your lamp. You've written
some message. That's what you have in your hand.
You keep putting on
the seal and taking it off again.
You write and then you
rub out what you've written.
You drop it to the ground, and tears

stream down your face.
From what I can see
despair appears to be driving you
out of your reason. Oh my king,
Agamemnon, tell me what it is.
I am a man of good will, I am
loyal to you, you can trust me with it.
I was in your
wedding procession, don't you remember,
back at the start. Tyndareos gave me
to your wife as part of the dowry,
because I could be trusted.

AGAMEMNON: Leda, the daughter of Thestios, had three
  girls of her own:
Phoibe, and my wife Clytemnestra,
and Helen.
And the highest-born young men in Greece came
asking to marry
Helen.
And threatened each other,
looking for blood. Each of them said
that if he himself did not get to marry her
he would murder whoever did.
So her father Tyndareos
could not think what he should do to avoid disaster.
Should he give her to one of them
or not let her marry at all?
Then he thought of a way.
The suitors would have to take an oath, all of them
together, a solemn oath, sealed
with a burnt offering,
swearing to defend whichever of them
should win Helen, Tyndareos' daughter, for his wife.
And if anyone
should ever carry her off, and keep

her husband from her bed, whether
he came from Greece or somewhere else, they would all
make war on his city and bring it to the ground.
So they swore. Old Tyndareos
was sharper than they were:
when it was over he left the choice to his daughter.
He said, "Now why shouldn't she marry
as the sweet breath of Aphrodite directs her?"
And her love fell—that's the pity of it—
on Menelaos.
It was later
that this Paris, who judged
the beauty of goddesses,
as the Argives tell it,
came from Phrygia to Sparta. There were gold flowers
stitched onto his clothes,
he glittered with barbarian jewels,
he loved her.
She returned it. While Menelaos was away
he carried her off with him
to the summer pastures of Ida.
Menelaos, stung by his fate, raged
through all Greece, reminding
everyone who had sworn that oath
that they were bound to come to his help now.
And the Greeks rushed to arms. And they have come
to the straits of Aulis
with their fighting gear, their ships, their shields,
their chariots, their horses.
And because Menelaos is my brother, they chose
me to be their general.
I wish they had saved the honor for someone else.
And when the whole army had mustered
here at Aulis,
the wind died. Calm. We still cannot sail.
There is only one hope of our going,

according to Kalchas,
the prophet. Iphigeneia, my daughter,
must be sacrificed to Artemis,
the deity of this place.
Then the wind will take us to Troy,
and the city will fall to us.
When I heard this I called Talthybios the herald
and said, "Sound the trumpet, sound it,
and tell them all to go home. I could never
make myself kill my own daughter."
But at that my brother started reasoning with me,
arguing, urging me
to commit this horror,
till I wrote a letter telling my wife
to send our daughter here
to be married to Achilles.
I told her
what a great man he is, and I said
he would not sail with us until a bride
from our own family
had been sent to his home in Phthia.
A story I made up
so that my wife would send the girl.
Among the Achaians the only ones who know
are Kalchas, Odysseus, and Menelaos.
And what I have done
is wrong, and I want to undo it. That is why
I wrote this second letter that you found me
sealing and unsealing. Take it. Go to Argos.
I will tell you what it says
since you are loyal to my wife and my house.   (*Reads.*)
"Clytemnestra, daughter of Leda,
I mean this letter to rule out the first one."   (*Pauses.*)

OLD MAN: Tell me the rest. Read it. Then I will be able
    to repeat the message myself
    as it is in the letter.

AGAMEMNON (*reads*): "Do not send your daughter
    to this folded harbor of Euboia,
    Aulis,
    a shore where no waves come in.
    We will find some other time for her marriage."

OLD MAN: But Achilles, when he learns
    there's no bride for him after all,
    will he not blaze up
    raging against you and your wife? That
    frightens me. How will you deal with that?

AGAMEMNON: Only his name has been used. Achilles himself
    knows nothing
    of our plans, the marriage,
    what I said about giving him my daughter
    as his bride.

OLD MAN: Then you promised her to the son of a goddess
    simply to fetch her here
    to be a victim for the Argives! King Agamemnon,
    your daring appalls me.

AGAMEMNON: I have lost the use of my reason! My ruin
    is straight ahead of me. No. Go. Start.
    Run. Never mind the age in your legs.

OLD MAN: I will lose no time, my lord.

AGAMEMNON: Do not pause at the springs in the shade,
    nor stop to sleep.

OLD MAN: The gods keep me from it!

AGAMEMNON: When you get to where roads fork, take a sharp look
down all of them. Make sure
no chariot slips past you,
too fast or not noticed,
bringing my daughter here to the Greek ships.

OLD MAN: It shall be done.

AGAMEMNON: If she has left the palace
and you meet her and her escort
make them turn back. Take
the reins yourself and shake them loose
and urge on the horses to Mycenae
where the Cyclopes built the walls.

OLD MAN: One thing. What will make your wife
and your daughter trust me
when I tell them the message?

AGAMEMNON: This seal, on the letter.
Take it, and go now. Day
is breaking. Already the sun's
chariot of fire has sent
brightness into the sky. Go. Take up
your task. We must all suffer.

(*The* OLD MAN *goes off right.*)

No mortal
ever knows happiness and good fortune all
the way to the end.
Each one is born with his bitterness waiting for him.

(He goes in through the main door.
The CHORUS *of young Chalkidian women*
enters left.)

CHORUS: I have crossed the narrows
   of Euripos, I came sailing and I beached
   at Aulis, on the sands. I left
   Chalkis, my city, where the spring
   of Arethousa wells up and runs flashing
   down to the sea. I came
   to see for myself this army of the Achaians,
   the oar-winged ships of the heroes,
   the thousand galleys
   which blond Menelaos and Agamemnon of the same
   great lineage sent,
   as our husbands tell us,
   to fetch Helen again:
   Helen.
   Whom Paris the herdsman seized
   from the reedy bank of the river Eurotas
   where Aphrodite had led her for him, after
   the goddess had bathed in the dewy fountain
   and taken her place beside
   Hera and Pallas Athene
   for her beauty to be judged.
   Through the grove
   where the victims die on the altar
   of Artemis I came
   running, and I blushed for shyness
   at my fever to see
   the pitched strength of the Danaans, the tents
   hung with weapons, the clanging
   press of armed horsemen.
   Now I set eyes
   on the two that are named Aias, I see
   Oïleus' son and that son of Telamon

who is the hope of Salamis,
and with them Protesilaos,
and Palamedes, child of Poseidon's son,
hunched down, weaving
their cunning into a game of draughts.
Near them is Diomedes
delighting in throwing the discus,
and Meriones, scion of Ares,
wonder of men. Laërtes' son
has come there from his craggy island,
and Nireus, most handsome of the Achaians.
I have seen wind-footed Achilles
in full armor racing over the sands:
Thetis' son, whom Cheiron reared,
and he was racing against horses,
four of them, and a chariot, on the curved track.
I saw the beauty of those horses, gold
worked into their bits and bridles,
the yoke pair dappled
gray with white in their manes, the trace horses
bays with dappled white fetlocks;
and Eumelos, the grandson of Pheres,
driving them, shouting,
goading them on faster, and they
hugged the turns, but Peleus' son
in all his armor stayed with them the whole way,
never falling behind the chariot rail and the axle,
and won.
And I came to where the ships lie. Even a god
would find no words for the way that sight
stirs a woman's eyes. Pleasure took my breath away.
The fleet of the Myrmidons from Phthia, fifty
lean vessels, lay to the right
bearing statues
of the sea-god's daughters, the Nereïds, in gold,
high on their sterns,

to show that those ships were Achilles'.
Next to them lay the galleys of the Argives,
their admiral
Mekisteus' son, whom Talaos
brought up to manhood;
and Sthenelos, Kapaneus' son, was there.
Then the sixty ships from Attica; the son
of Theseus is their commander, and their ensign
is Pallas Athene with her winged chariot
and its horses, a sign which lightens the hearts
of mariners.
Then the flotilla of fifty ships
from Boiotia with their ensign rising
from each of the sterns: Kadmos
holding a dragon of gold. Leïtos,
born of the earth,
is their admiral. And the same number
of ships from Lokris, commanded by the son
of Oïleus, who had come
from the famous city of Thronion
to moor beside them.
The son of Atreus had brought a hundred vessels
from Mycenae
where the Cyclopes built the walls. The king
his brother and companion-in-command,
sailed with him to bring vengeance
on the bride who had abandoned his house
to lie with a barbarian. I saw the ships
from Pylos, that Gerenian Nestor brought,
and their sign is the river
Alpheios, that flows
by his country, shown on his sterns
in the form of a bull. Then the twelve
Ainian vessels that obey King Gouneus,
and near them the lords of Elis, who are called
the Epeians: Eurytos commands

the ships that came with them.
And the white-oared Taphian galleys followed
King Meges, Phyleus' son, from the rocky islands
of Echinai that frighten sailors.
To the left
the twelve sleek galleys of Aias of Salamis
made up the end of the line
that ran back down the beach
without a break, beside the army. The barbarian
who joins battle with these should not
cling to his hopes of sailing home.
I have seen the whole fleet,
and when it is famous and they
tell of it where I live
I will remember.

> (MENELAOS *and the* OLD MAN
> *enter right, quarreling.*)

OLD MAN: Menelaos, you have no right to do this!

MENELAOS: Get away! You are too loyal to your master.

OLD MAN: Your reproach does me honor.

MENELAOS: You'll be sorry if you go on meddling.

OLD MAN: You had no right
to open the letter I was carrying.

MENELAOS: And you had no right to carry a letter
that would harm the Greek cause.

OLD MAN: Argue with others about that.
Give me the letter.

MENELAOS: I will not.

OLD MAN (*seizes him*): Then I won't let go.

MENELAOS: I'll bloody your head with my scepter.

OLD MAN: What greater glory than to die for my master?

MENELAOS: Let go! Your words are too big for a slave.

OLD MAN (*calling in at the main door of the tent*): Master!
    Help! This man
snatched your letter out of my hand,
Agamemnon! Mutiny!

>   (AGAMEMNON *enters from the main door.*)

AGAMEMNON: What is this? Brawling and arguing
    outside my tent door?

MENELAOS: My voice takes precedence here, I believe.

>   (*At a sign from* AGAMEMNON, *the* OLD MAN
>   *goes in at the right-hand side door.*)

AGAMEMNON: How did you come to quarrel
    with this old man, Menelaos?
    And why were you so violent with him?

MENELAOS: Look at me, Agamemnon. Then I will
    start to tell you.

AGAMEMNON: Do you think I'm afraid
    to look you in the eye, Menelaos?
    I am a son of Atreus.

MENELAOS: Do you see this letter? It was meant
    to betray all of us.

AGAMEMNON: That letter—in the first place
  give it back to me.

MENELAOS: Not until I have told the Greeks what it says.

AGAMEMNON: You mean you broke the seal. So you know
  what you have no business knowing.

MENELAOS: Yes I broke the seal. And it's you
  who will suffer as a result, for acting
  behind our backs.

AGAMEMNON: How did you come to find him? Oh gods
  what shamelessness!

MENELAOS: I was watching for the arrival
  of your daughter from Argos.

AGAMEMNON: You see? Shameless again! What right have you
  to spy on what concerns me?

MENELAOS: I choose to. I'm not your slave.

AGAMEMNON: This is beyond endurance! Am I not to be allowed
  to govern in my own house?

MENELAOS: No, because you're not to be trusted.
  You never were, you aren't to be trusted now,
  you will never be.

AGAMEMNON: How smooth you are with your slanders.
  I despise a nimble tongue.

MENELAOS: How do you feel about a mind
  true to nothing and no one? It is you
  who must answer for yourself. And don't try

to shout down the truth
just because you're angry.
I won't be too harsh with you.
Have you forgotten the fever
of your ambition at the first thought
of leading an army against Troy?
You pretended
not to want the command but really
you'd have paid anything to be general.
You know how you humbled yourself
at the time. Touching hands,
keeping open house to the whole
citizenry,
making them all speak to you, one by one,
whether they wanted to or not.
Anything
to entice preferment out of the crowd.
But once you'd been chosen to command, all that changed.
You dropped the friends you didn't need anymore.
It was hard to get to talk with you, you shut
yourself in.
Is one to admire a man
who changes as soon as he gets what he wants
and turns from friends
the moment he's in a position to help them?
That's the first point
in which I found you wanting, Agamemnon.
Next, you led the combined armies
of the Hellenes here to Aulis
and then at one stroke all your importance
collapsed
just because the wind fell.
You were nothing
if the gods would not fill your sails. And the Danaans
clamored for the ships to be sent home
and an end to these senseless efforts.

I haven't forgotten the sight
of your face when you heard that. What anguish,
what gloom at the thought
that you might not sail in, after all,
lord
of a thousand ships
flooding Priam's beach with arms. Then you asked me
to help you. "What shall I do? Isn't there
something I can do?" Anything
rather than lose the command
and the glory.
Then when Kalchas said, "Yes:
sacrifice your daughter to Artemis
and the Greek ships
will be able to sail,"
how happy you were to promise.
And no one—admit it—forced you
to write to your wife
and tell her to send the girl here,
pretending that she would marry Achilles.
Then you change your mind,
you unburden yourself of a different message
and it's discovered.
At this point you'd never murder your daughter.
Well. This same sky
watched you speak otherwise. It's true
men find this happening to them
all the time. They sweat and clamber
for power until it's theirs,
then all at once they
fall back and amount to nothing again.
Sometimes it's the fault of the populace,
too stupid to know who's talking sense.
Other times it's richly deserved: the leaders
turn out not to be able
to keep the city safe.

I grieve above all
for Greece and her mortification.
She had set her heart on glory. Now
she will have nothing to answer
when the barbarian trash laugh at her,
thanks to you and your daughter.
Oh I would never put a man at the head
of a country or an army
just because of his connections.
A general needs to have a mind.

CHORUS: It is terrible when discord
divides brothers
and they fight each other with words.

AGAMEMNON: It's my turn now. And I'll keep my
reproach dignified: brief,
restrained.
Not staring wide, shamelessly, but with
modesty, remembering that you
are my brother. No man who amounts to anything
is without a sense of shame. You
come to me in a passion,
breathing hard, eyes
suffused with blood. Tell me, who
has wronged you? What do you want? Are you pining
for a virtuous wife? I'm afraid
I can't do much for you there. The one you had
is no credit to your government.
Am I, then, supposed to suffer
for your shortcomings
when they're no fault of mine? It's not
my ambition that is biting you.
You care about nothing,
nothing but holding a beautiful woman in your arms.
You've abandoned all decency, all sense.

The passions of a degraded man are degraded.
And if I was mistaken to start with, and later
was wise enough to change my mind,
is that madness? No, you're the one who's mad.
The gods in their kindness took a bad wife off your hands
and you're trying to get her back.
The suitors, it's true,
were so misguided
as to swear an oath to Tyndareos
while the lust was on them. In my view
some goddess—Hope, I imagine—accomplished that.
Not you in any case.
Still, lead them, by all means
to fight your war for you. They're foolish enough
to stick to their oaths. But the gods
will not be fooled. They can recognize
oaths that were set up as traps, and sworn to
under duress.
I will not kill my children.
There's no justice in things turning out
precisely the way you want them to—you get
your vengeance on a worthless wife—
while my days and nights melt
in tears, at the unholy
crimes I've committed against my own children.
These are the few things
I wanted to say to you once and for all.
You should be able to understand them.
You can refuse
to be sensible if you want to. But for my part
I will set straight my own affairs.

CHORUS: This is not what was said before.
  But the change
  is for the better:
  refusing to harm a child.

MENELAOS: Oh misery! Then I see I have no friends.

AGAMEMNON: When you have friends you try to destroy them.

MENELAOS: Is there no way that you will show
    that you are my father's son?

AGAMEMNON: I will share your reason, not your madness.

MENELAOS: You would share my troubles, if you were a
    brother and a friend.

AGAMEMNON: Say that when you have behaved like a brother
    and a friend to me,
not when you are doing me harm.

MENELAOS: And Greece—you mean you'll abandon her now
    to her struggle?

AGAMEMNON: Greece has been driven mad by the same god
    who drove you out of your senses.

MENELAOS: Congratulate yourself on your scepter
    now that you've betrayed your own brother.
    I'll find some other way, other friends—

                    (*Enter a* MESSENGER *right.*)

MESSENGER: Commander of all the armies of Greece, King
    Agamemnon, I have brought you,
    from home, your daughter
    whom you called Iphigeneia.
    And her mother, your Clytemnestra, is with her,
    and the boy Orestes. You've been away from home
    a long time, and the sight of them
    will be a joy to you.

It's been a tiring journey, and they are resting
now, bathing their soft feet
at the flowing spring,
and the horses are resting too;
we turned them loose to graze there in the good pasture.
I came on ahead to tell you,
so that you would be ready. But rumor
travels faster. The army knows
your daughter is here. And they are running
and crowding to get a look at the girl;
everyone wants to catch a glimpse
of those whom fortune has blessed.
They say, "Is there going to be a wedding,
or did King Agamemnon miss the child
so much that he sent for her?" Others say,
"Offerings are being made
consecrating the child to Artemis,
goddess of Aulis,
as though for a wedding, but who
will be the bridegroom?" Come. Do
what comes next, Agamemnon. Bring the sacrificial
basket, and lead the procession
around the altar. Set the garlands on your heads.
King Menelaos, prepare
the marriage feast. Let the flute
trill within doors and the floor
resound with the dancing, for this is the day
that dawned to see your child made happy.

AGAMEMNON: Thank you. You may go inside. What is left to do
no doubt will turn out well, in the course of fate.

(*The* MESSENGER *goes in at the right-hand door.*)

Oh miserable creature that I am,
now what can I say? Where

can I begin in the face of this misery?
I have fallen into the snare of fate.
I laid my plan, but I was outwitted
from the start by the cunning of destiny.
How fortunate are the humbly born.
They can shed tears when they need to, they can tell
all their grief. But those of our station
are not allowed to appear
undignified. We are the slaves of the mob we lead,
molded by the pomp we must show in public.
I am ashamed
of my tears. But in the presence of this
enormity I am ashamed not to weep.
And my wife—
what words can I find, when I see her? How
will I greet her? With what eyes
will I welcome her? It was terrible
enough. Why did she have to come here too
when I never sent for her? But it is natural
for her to come here with her daughter,
to be present, the bride's mother,
to give her child in marriage.
And that's how she will learn of my treachery.
But the unhappy
girl. Girl? Why do I call her a girl?
When it seems that Hades
is about to make her his wife. Oh I
pity her. I can hear her
calling out to me, "Father!
Are you going to kill me? I hope that you
and everyone you love are married like this."
And Orestes will be there too, scarcely
old enough to walk, and he will
scream cries without words,
but my heart will know what they mean.
Oh what ruin Priam's son

Paris has brought me! All this he called down
by winning the love of Helen.

CHORUS: Grief lays hands on me too,
though I am a stranger, and a woman, and these
are a king's troubles.

MENELAOS: Brother, give me your hand.

AGAMEMNON: Here is my hand. You have won. I must bear
the loss.

MENELAOS: I swear by Pelops, whom our father
called "Father," and by Atreus himself
who sired us both, that I will
speak to you now openly, as I feel,
without any hidden object in mind,
but speaking from my heart. When I saw the tears
running from your eyes
I felt tears of my own
and pity. I will not set myself against you
any longer. I call back what I said before.
I am with you now, and I add my voice
to yours: do not
kill your child, not for my sake.
It cannot be just for you to suffer
so that I can be satisfied,
nor for your children to die
while mine fill their eyes with the light.
What do I need after all? Could I not find
a wife who would do me credit
if I chose to marry again? Am I to lose
a brother, whom I should treasure, merely to win back
Helen,
buying evil with good?
I was rash. I behaved like a child, until

I came close to the thing itself
and saw what it means, to kill one's own child.
Then pity overcame me. For the girl
from my own family who was going to lose her life
because of my marriage. What has your daughter
to do with Helen? Let the army
break up and leave Aulis. Brother,
no more tears, now. Yours are the cause of mine.
Whatever the oracles say of your daughter,
from now on it concerns you, not me.
I give you my share in it. You can see how long
my threats lasted. I admit
I changed my mind. But that's
natural if a man loves his brother.
At every step I've tried to see
the right way to act.
That's not the vacillation of a weakling.

CHORUS: Your words are noble. They are worthy
of your ancestors.
Tantalos himself, the son of Zeus,
might well have been proud of them.

AGAMEMNON: Menelaos, thank you. I never could have hoped
that you would speak as you have spoken now.
But what you have said is right
and worthy of you. Discord
flares up between brothers
over love or the family estate.
It is poisonous to both sides. I hate it.
But I have reached a point where circumstances
leave me no choice. I shall be
forced to shed her blood,
to kill my daughter.

MENELAOS: Forced? Who can make you kill the girl?

AGAMEMNON: The combined armies of the Achaians.

MENELAOS: Not if you've sent her home
  to Argos.

AGAMEMNON: I might be able to do that
  without anyone knowing. But afterward—

MENELAOS: What? You're wrong
  to go in such dread of the mob.

AGAMEMNON: Kalchas will tell the whole army
  what was prophesied.

MENELAOS: Not if he's dead. And that's a simple matter.

AGAMEMNON: The tribe of prophets wants only to be
    important,
  the whole rotten crowd of them.

MENELAOS: When they don't prophesy
  they're useless, and when they do
  it does no good.

AGAMEMNON: But aren't you afraid of something,
  something I've just remembered?

MENELAOS: Not unless you tell me what it is.

AGAMEMNON: Someone else
  knows everything. The son of Sisyphos,
  Odysseus.

MENELAOS: There's no reason for Odysseus
  to do anything to injure you or me.

AGAMEMNON: He's cunning, and it always turns out
    that he and the crowd are on the same side.

MENELAOS: He loves power. A terrible love.

AGAMEMNON: Can't you see him rising
    to his feet in the middle of the Argives
    and repeating
    the oracles that Kalchas spelled out to us,
    telling how I promised
    the sacrifice to Artemis
    and then failed to keep my promise?
    Can't you see
    his words sweeping the whole army along with him
    when he tells them
    to kill you, kill me, and then sacrifice the girl themselves?
    Even if I
    could escape to Argos, they would follow me there.
    They'd tear the city to the ground,
    even the great walls that the Cyclopes built.
    You see why I'm in despair. Almighty gods, how helpless
    you have made me now!
    There is nothing I can do. But you, Menelaos,
    when you go back to the camp,
    save me from one thing at least.
    Take care that Clytemnestra
    learns nothing of all this,
    until I take my child and give her to Hades.
    Let me suffer my ordeal
    with as few tears as possible.
    And you, women of Chalkis,
    you will do well to say nothing.

                  (MENELAOS *goes off left.* AGAMEMNON
                   goes in at the central door.)

CHORUS: Blessed are they
    who share the delights of Aphrodite
    and are not burned alive by them, moderate
    and happy,
    whom the passion has not stung into madness, at whom
    the archer with the golden hair,
    Eros, has not aimed
    desire in his two arrows, the one
    striking rapture, the other
    devastation. Oh Cyprian,
    most beautiful of the goddesses, keep
    such wild flights from me.
    Let me know love
    within reason, and desire within
    marriage, and feel your presence
    not your rage.
    The natures of humans
    are various, and human ways of acting
    are different,
    but everyone knows what is right,
    and teaching
    inclines them at last to virtue.
    Humility is wisdom,
    making us see the right way
    as something beautiful.
    And from this beauty honor is born
    and life earns immortal fame.
    It is a great thing, the pursuit of virtue:
    in women it is a stillness
    in their love;
    among men, multiplied
    ten thousand times among citizens,
    it makes a city great.
    Oh Paris, they took you as a baby
    to grow up herding white heifers on Mount Ida,
    making on reeds a barbarous

music, a thin echo
of the Phrygian pipes of Olympos.
The milk-laden cattle
never stopped grazing when the goddesses
stood forth for you to judge their beauty.
You chose
madness, and madness brought you
here to Greece, to the palace
inlaid with ivory,
and to the eyes of Helen
that took your gaze full of love and returned it.
And from that rose the dispute that sends
the armed Greeks in their ships
to sack Troy.

(CLYTEMNESTRA, IPHIGENEIA, *and* ORESTES *enter
in a chariot escorted by the* ATTENDANTS.)

ATTENDANTS: Oh great is the fortune
of the great!
See, the king's daughter, Iphigeneia,
my queen.
And Tyndareos' daughter, Clytemnestra. How great
were their ancestors! How momentous
the occasion that brings them here!
Those who excel in power and in wealth
are gods, in the eyes
of mortals less favored by fortune.

CHORUS (*moving to the chariot*): Let us stand here, women of
Chalkis,
and hand the queen down from her chariot.
Make sure she does not stumble.
Gently, carefully, help with our hands,
let us help Agamemnon's
noble child to

descend unafraid for her first steps in Aulis.
(*To the occupants of the chariot.*)
We too are strangers here. Gently, quietly,
we welcome the strangers from Argos.

CLYTEMNESTRA: I think your kind greeting is a good omen.
I have come here bringing
this girl, as I hope, to a happy marriage.
(*To the* ATTENDANTS.)
Take from the chariot
the gifts I brought with her, her dowry.
Carry them in and set them down carefully.

(*The* ATTENDANTS *carry the gifts into the tent.*)

Daughter, come from the chariot, alight
on your delicate feet. And you,
young women, give her your arms, help her down.
Someone do the same for me,
as I step from the chariot. Someone stand
in front of the horses' yoke.
A colt's eye takes fright
if there is no one to reassure it.
This is Agamemnon's son. The baby
Orestes. Take him.
Are you still asleep, my child,
lulled by the rocking of the chariot?
When you wake, wake happily. This is your sister's
wedding day. You had
noble forebears, you will have
a noble kinsman: the sea-nymph's son
who is like his ancestors the gods.

(CLYTEMNESTRA *hands* ORESTES *to a member of
the* CHORUS, *descends, takes* ORESTES *again, and sets
him down at her feet. As she speaks the next lines*
AGAMEMNON *enters through the main door.*)

Sit here by my feet, child. Iphigeneia,
come to your mother. Stand close
and show these strangers
what reason I have to be happy. Now
here comes your dear father. Greet him.

IPHIGENEIA (*starts to run to* AGAMEMNON, *then turns to*
CLYTEMNESTRA): Mother, don't be angry
if I run from you
to be the first to embrace him.

CLYTEMNESTRA (*speaking at the same time*): Oh most revered
in my eyes, Agamemnon, King,
you commanded us to come, and we are here.

IPHIGENEIA (*running to* AGAMEMNON): I want to run and put
my arms around you,
Father, after such a long time!
How I have missed your face! Don't be angry!

CLYTEMNESTRA: It's as it should be, child. You were always,
of all the children I bore him, the one
who loved your father most.

IPHIGENEIA: Father, how happy I am to see you.
It has been so long.

AGAMEMNON: And I am happy to see you, Iphigeneia.
The same words rise to my lips.

IPHIGENEIA: Oh, if you could be as happy as I am! Father,
what a wonderful thing
to have brought me here to you.

AGAMEMNON: Perhaps my child. Perhaps.

IPHIGENEIA: How troubled your eyes look, yet you say
you are happy to see me.

AGAMEMNON: A king and a general
has many burdens.

IPHIGENEIA: Oh forget them, forget them for now. I am here.
Put them aside and be with me.

AGAMEMNON: I am with you. I am nowhere else.

IPHIGENEIA: Then don't frown anymore.
I want those lines to leave your face.

AGAMEMNON: See. How happy I am to look at you.

IPHIGENEIA: But your eyes are overflowing with tears.

AGAMEMNON: We will be separated
for so long.

IPHIGENEIA: I don't understand what you mean.
Dear father, I don't understand.

AGAMEMNON: If you understood I would feel even worse.

IPHIGENEIA: Then we'll talk and I won't understand,
if that will make you happier.

AGAMEMNON: Oh! (*aside*) I can't contain my suffering!
(*aloud*) Thank you.

IPHIGENEIA: Stay home, Father. Stay with your children.

AGAMEMNON: I want to. But I can't do what I
   want to
   and it makes me unhappy.

IPHIGENEIA: Oh I wish there were no more
   spears, no more
   of this grievance that's come to Menelaos!

AGAMEMNON: Before they are done
   they will destroy others as they have me.

IPHIGENEIA: Father, how long you've been
   shut away in Aulis!

AGAMEMNON: And even now something
   prevents me from sending the army on its way.

IPHIGENEIA: Where do they say
   the Trojans live, Father?

AGAMEMNON: In the country where Priam has a son,
   a son named Paris
   who I wish had never been born.

IPHIGENEIA: You are going all that way, Father,
   leaving me behind.

AGAMEMNON: Now you see
   what you did not understand before.

IPHIGENEIA: Oh if only it were proper for me to go with you!

AGAMEMNON: You will think of your father
on your own long voyage.

IPHIGENEIA: Will my mother come with me
or will I be alone?

AGAMEMNON: Neither father nor mother. Alone.

IPHIGENEIA: You won't make me live
somewhere else, will you, Father?

AGAMEMNON: I have said enough. Too much. Girls
are not meant to know about such things.

IPHIGENEIA: When you have finished what you have to do
at Troy, Father,
sail straight home to me.

AGAMEMNON: Before that
I must make a sacrifice. Here in Aulis.

IPHIGENEIA: Sacrifices are to find out
how we may please the gods.

AGAMEMNON: You will see. You will stand by the font
of purifying water.

IPHIGENEIA: Will we dance around the altar?

AGAMEMNON: How I envy you, knowing nothing!
Now go in. It's better
for young girls not to be seen.
Give me a kiss, and your right hand.
You will soon be far away from your father,

and for a long time.
Oh breast, cheeks, oh blonde head,
what a crushing weight
Helen and the Trojan city
have called down upon you!
I must not touch you anymore.
It sets the tears flowing. Go in.

(IPHIGENEIA *goes in at the left-hand door.*)

Daughter of Leda, forgive me
for this access of grief
at giving my child in marriage to Achilles.
Partings such as these are happy, of course,
but when a father must send
his daughter to the house of another
after all his years of watching over her
it cuts into the heart.

CLYTEMNESTRA: I feel it too. I'm not so foolish as to reproach you
for grieving. I will feel just the same,
you know, when I lead the child
out into the marriage hymns,
so I don't blame you.
But time will heal the sadness. It's the custom and
we will get used to it. Tell me
about his ancestors, and where he was born.
All I know is his name.

AGAMEMNON: To Asopos
a daughter was born, named Aigina.

CLYTEMNESTRA: Who married her? A mortal, a god?

AGAMEMNON: Zeus himself. And she bore him a son,
Aiakos, king of the island of Oinone.

CLYTEMNESTRA: And which of his children succeeded him?

AGAMEMNON: Peleus. He married one of the daughters
of Nereus, the sea-god.

CLYTEMNESTRA: With her father's blessings, or did Peleus
take her in defiance of the gods?

AGAMEMNON: Zeus made the betrothal, and gave her in
marriage.
He has the authority.

CLYTEMNESTRA: Where were they married?
Under the waves of the ocean?

AGAMEMNON: At the foot of Pelion,
the sacred mountain where Cheiron lives.

CLYTEMNESTRA: In the country where they say the centaurs
live?

AGAMEMNON: There all the gods came to the marriage of
Peleus
and the wedding feast.

CLYTEMNESTRA: And was it Thetis or his father Peleus
who brought Achilles up?

AGAMEMNON: It was Cheiron,
to keep him from learning the evil ways of men.

CLYTEMNESTRA: Wise teacher! And Peleus was wiser still,
sending the boy to him.

AGAMEMNON: Such is the man who will be your daughter's
husband.

CLYTEMNESTRA: He sounds acceptable. Where in Greece is he from?

AGAMEMNON: From Phthia, on the river Apidanos.

CLYTEMNESTRA: And that is where he will take our daughter?

AGAMEMNON: That is for him to decide.

CLYTEMNESTRA: May it be a happy marriage!
    When will it take place?

AGAMEMNON: At the full moon.
    That is the most propitious time.

CLYTEMNESTRA: Have you made our daughter's
    sacrifice to the goddess?

AGAMEMNON: I will. We had just come to that.

CLYTEMNESTRA: And afterward you will have the marriage
    feast?

AGAMEMNON: When I have offered the gods
    the sacrifice they require of me.

CLYTEMNESTRA: And where shall I prepare the women's
    banquet?

AGAMEMNON: Here. By the high sterns of the ships from Argos.

CLYTEMNESTRA: Here? Well, there is no choice. I hope
    good fortune comes of it.

AGAMEMNON: Do you know what you should do?
    Please do it.

CLYTEMNESTRA: What do you want? You know I'm not in the habit
of disobeying you.

AGAMEMNON: Then here, in the presence of the bridegroom,
we men will—

CLYTEMNESTRA: You? Will I not be there
for the things a bride's mother must do?

AGAMEMNON: I will give away your child. The army and I.

CLYTEMNESTRA: And where will I be when that happens?

AGAMEMNON: In Argos, taking care of your daughters.

CLYTEMNESTRA: Leaving my child here? And who
will raise the bridal torch?

AGAMEMNON: I will provide the light, all the light
proper for the bridal pair.

CLYTEMNESTRA: That is wrong, wrong. And such things are
important.

AGAMEMNON: It is not right for you to stay here
jostling among the soldiers.

CLYTEMNESTRA: It is right that I should give
my children in marriage. I am their mother.

AGAMEMNON: It is not right for our daughters at home
to be left alone.

CLYTEMNESTRA: They are well looked after,
safe in their part of the palace.

AGAMEMNON: Please do it.

CLYTEMNESTRA: No, by the goddess who reigns in Argos.
 You see to the things outside
 that concern you. I'll go in
 and see to the preparations for my daughter's wedding.

(She goes in at the left-hand door.)

AGAMEMNON: Oh, it was no use. I tried but I failed
 to send my wife out of my sight.
 I contrive plots, I lay plans to deceive
 those dearest to me
 and it all comes to nothing.
 Now I must arrange with Kalchas, who performs
 our sacrifices,
 the thing which the goddess demands
 and I hate the thought of.
 I owe it to Greece.
 A wise man supports in his house
 a good and faithful wife. Or no wife at all.

(He goes off left.)

CHORUS: Now they will sail
 to Simoïs where the waters spin silver,
 the Greeks in pride of numbers,
 of ships, of weapons. They will come
 to Ilion, to the plains below Troy
 shining in the blessing of Apollo,
 where Kassandra, they say, flings
 like sunlight the blonde falls of her hair
 from under the green laurel when the god
 grips her and she shakes
 and sees what is to come.
 At Troy on the ramparts, on the circling

walls, drawn up,
the Trojans will be waiting
as Ares in his bronze battle gear
comes nearer with the falling oars,
the hanging prows riffling the estuary mouths
of Simoïs. What he will want
is Helen, the sister
of the twin sons of Zeus, the Dioskouroi,
who are stars in heaven.
To possess her again out of Priam's kingdom,
the prize
of the Achaians' spears, shields, labors in battle,
and bring her once more into Greece.
The god will girdle with slaughter
the stone-cased stronghold
of Pergamos, the Phrygians' city. He will see
Priam's head hewn from its shoulders
and every house in Troy
smashed and rummaged. Then what a crying
from the girls and from Priam's queen.
And Helen herself, the daughter of Zeus,
will taste tears for the day she left her husband.
Oh may such anguish never befall us,
women of Chalkis, nor our children's children,
as shall then work through the Lydian women
for all their gold,
and through the wives of Phrygia so that they
stand by the looms saying, "Who now
will wrap his wrist in my swaying hair and uproot me
out of my ruined home,
dragging me through my tears?
It is all thanks to you, daughter
of the swan with the sinuous neck, whose wings
hid Zeus from Leda,
if that is true.
It is still you

even if that is no more than a story
out of the books of the Muses,
with no meaning."

(*Enter* ACHILLES *left, unarmed and dressed with
ostentatious simplicity. He looks about
twenty-five years old.*)

ACHILLES: Where is the commander of the Achaians?
Will one of his servants tell him that Peleus' son
Achilles is standing at his door?
It is not the same for all of us
having to wait here
by the straits. Some of us,
who have no wives, sit here by the shore, having left
empty houses at home. Others, who are married,
still have no children.
Such is the frenzy that has seized Greece
for this war,
not without the consent of the gods.
With things at this pass, let me say
what is due to me. Anyone else who wants to
may speak in his own behalf. I came away
from Pharsalia, I left Peleus,
to be kept waiting for
a wind, beside the straits,
trying to keep my men quiet, my Myrmidons:
day after day they come up to me and say, "Achilles,
what is keeping us here? How much more
time must we waste on this expedition to Troy?
Do what you came here to do
or else lead the army home.
Don't wait for the sons of Atreus."

(CLYTEMNESTRA *enters from the left-hand door.*)

CLYTEMNESTRA: Son of the Nereïd, I heard your voice
  and came out to greet you.

ACHILLES: Oh sacred modesty, who
  is this beautiful woman?

CLYTEMNESTRA: You could hardly expect to recognize me
  since you never saw me before,
  but your regard for modesty is commendable.

ACHILLES: Who are you? And why have you come
  to the camp of the Greek army,
  you a woman, here among the shields?

CLYTEMNESTRA: I am the daughter of Leda,
  Clytemnestra. Agamemnon is my husband.

ACHILLES: Brief and to the point.
  But it is not seemly for me
  to be seen talking with women.

(*He starts to go off left.*)

CLYTEMNESTRA: Wait. Why do you run away? (*following him*)
  Give me your right hand—here is mine:
  a happy beginning to this betrothal of ours!

ACHILLES (*turns politely, then recoils in horror*): Do you know
    what you are saying? Touch
  your hand? How could I face Agamemnon
  if I touch what heaven forbids me to touch?

CLYTEMNESTRA: Why do you say heaven forbids it,
  son of Thetis the sea-nymph,
  when you are about to marry my daughter?

ACHILLES: Marry? Lady, what do you mean?
I am left with no answer. Has some delusion
led your mind astray?

CLYTEMNESTRA: I know it is natural
for men to be shy, faced with new kin
and the talk of marriage.

ACHILLES: Lady, I have never courted your daughter,
and the sons of Atreus have not spoken
one word to me about marriage.

CLYTEMNESTRA: What does this mean?
Indeed my words must be shocking to you
as your words are shocking to me.

ACHILLES: We must both find the explanation. There must be
some truth under what we both said.

CLYTEMNESTRA: I have been deceived. It seems
I have been preparing a marriage
that exists only in my mind.
I am filled with shame.

ACHILLES: Perhaps someone is amusing himself
with both of us.
Ignore it. It doesn't matter.

CLYTEMNESTRA: I will take my leave. I am humiliated.
I have been made to lie.
I can no longer look you in the face.

(*She starts to go in at the left-hand door.*)

ACHILLES: Lady, goodbye. I shall go in
to see your husband.

> (*He starts to go in at the main entrance, then
> pauses as he hears the* OLD MAN *call through the
> right-hand door.* CLYTEMNESTRA *pauses also.*)

OLD MAN (*off*): Wait, stranger! Grandson of Aiakos,
son of the goddess, you
I'm calling, and you, daughter of Leda.

ACHILLES: Who is that, shouting through the doorway?
How shaken he sounds!

OLD MAN: I am a slave. That's the truth, why not say it?
Fate has given me no choice.

ACHILLES: Whose slave? Not mine, certainly, here
among Agamemnon's possessions.

OLD MAN: That lady's, in front of the tent.
I was given to her by Tyndareos, her father.

ACHILLES: Well, here I am. Why did you want me to stay?

OLD MAN: Is there no one else here
besides you and her?

ACHILLES: We are alone. Come out from the king's tent. Speak.

OLD MAN: What I most feared has come to pass. Oh destiny,
(*entering*) spare those I pray for!

ACHILLES: Your words sound ominous,
and the message, it seems, is important.

CLYTEMNESTRA: Don't wait to kiss my hand. What did you
want to tell me?

OLD MAN: You know me, lady. You know my
devotion to you and your children.

CLYTEMNESTRA: I know you've been a servant in the palace
for a long time.

OLD MAN: I came to King Agamemnon
as part of your dowry.

CLYTEMNESTRA: Yes, you came with us to Argos
and you've always belonged to me.

OLD MAN: I have. And I put your interests
ahead of your husband's.

CLYTEMNESTRA: Now tell us. What is your secret?

OLD MAN: Your daughter. Her father
is going to kill her.
With his own hand.

CLYTEMNESTRA: What? I spit against what you say, old man!
You're out of your senses!

OLD MAN: He will plunge a blade into her white throat.

CLYTEMNESTRA: Oh, torment! Has he gone mad?

OLD MAN: No, he is sane about everything except you
and your child. There he's lost his reason.

CLYTEMNESTRA: Why? What demon could prompt him to such
a thing?

OLD MAN: The oracle. According to Kalchas. Saying
what must happen before the fleet can sail.

CLYTEMNESTRA: What horror is coming to me, and the child
whose father will kill her! Sail where?

OLD MAN: To the country of Dardanos, for Menelaos
to bring back Helen.

CLYTEMNESTRA: So the fates have woven Iphigeneia's death
into Helen's homecoming?

OLD MAN: Now you know it all. He intends
to sacrifice your daughter to Artemis.

CLYTEMNESTRA: And the talk of marriage, which brought me
here?

OLD MAN: The king knew you would bring her, and gladly,
to marry Achilles.

CLYTEMNESTRA: Oh daughter, you have come here
to your death, and your mother with you.

OLD MAN: The child's fate is terrible. So is yours.
It is a monstrous decision, Agamemnon's.

CLYTEMNESTRA: I am helpless. I am lost. Whatever I do
the tears come.

OLD MAN: If losing a child is painful, you have
reason for tears.

CLYTEMNESTRA: But where did you learn all this, old man?
How did it come to your ears?

OLD MAN: I was sent to you with a second letter
about the first one.

CLYTEMNESTRA: Telling me again to bring the girl here
to die, or warning me not to?

OLD MAN: Warning you not to. At that moment
your husband was in his right mind.

CLYTEMNESTRA: If you had such a letter for me
why was it not delivered?

OLD MAN: Menelaos took it from me.
All your troubles come from him.

CLYTEMNESTRA: Son of Thetis and Peleus,
have you heard this?

ACHILLES: I have heard the cause of your grief,
and I do not take lightly
the way I have been involved in the matter.

CLYTEMNESTRA: They are going to kill my child.
They tricked her with this talk of marrying you.

ACHILLES: I too blame Agamemnon,
and not only for the reasons you speak of.

CLYTEMNESTRA (*dropping to her knees and embracing* ACHILLES'
legs): Son of a goddess, I, a mortal,
am not ashamed to clasp your knees. What good
would pride do me now? What matters more to me
than my daughter's life?
Son of a goddess, save us: me
in my wretchedness,

and Iphigeneia, who they said was your betrothed,
even though it was not true.
I myself put the bridal wreath on her head for you,
I brought her here to be married,
and now I am leading her to her death.
You will be blamed if you do nothing to defend her.

(She rises, puts her left hand to ACHILLES' *cheek,*
and takes his right hand in her own.)

Even though you were never married to her
you were called her husband.
I implore you by your beard, by your right hand,
by your own mother. Your name, Achilles,
destroyed me; now you must clear it.

(Kneels and takes his knees again.)

There is no altar where I can take refuge,
none except your knees.
No friend smiles on me here. You have heard
of Agamemnon's raw heartlessness.
Nothing is sacred to him.
And I am a woman, come
into a camp of sailors, hard to control
and ripe for any crime—though they can be
useful enough when they want to be.
If you can bring yourself to stretch out
your hand over me, we are saved.
If not, we are lost.

CHORUS: Giving birth is a mystery. It casts
a powerful spell over mothers. All, all of them
without exception
will risk any suffering
for the sake of one of their children.

ACHILLES: Pride rises up in me
and draws me on. But I have learned
to curb my grief in adversity, and my joy
in triumph.
Mortals who have learned this
can hope to live by reason. There are moments
when it is good not to be too wise,
but there are times too when taking thought is useful.
I was brought up in the house of Cheiron,
the most righteous of men,
and he taught me to act from a simple heart.
If the commands of the sons of Atreus
are just, I will obey them. If not,
I will refuse. But whether here
or in Troy, I will remain free,
and in my fighting will bring credit on the war god
with my whole strength. As for you,
you have been treated cruelly
by those closest to you,
and as far as is proper for me, I shall extend
my pity to cover you. Never shall your daughter,
who has been called my betrothed,
be slaughtered by her father. He shall not use
me in his manipulations.
That way my name would be her butcher
as surely as if it had drawn the sword.
Your husband is the cause of this, but my own
body would be defiled
if through me that girl were to die,
horribly, brutally used, as she
has been. It fills me with rage
to think how she has been treated. I would be
the lowest of the Argives, a nothing,
and Menelaos a hero,
I would be no son of Peleus, but some
demon's offspring, if I

let my name do your husband's killing for him.
I swear by Nereus, whom the waves cradled, father
of Thetis who gave me birth,
King Agamemnon shall not touch your daughter
nor so much as graze her gown
with his fingertips,
or that barbarous settlement in Lydia,
Sipylos, where his sires
first saw the light,
is a Grecian city,
and no one has heard of Phthia.
This Kalchas, their prophet, will find
a bitter taste in the barley
and the lustral water before that sacrifice.
What is a prophet? Someone
who utters one truth in a flock of lies,
if he's lucky, and if he's not
everybody forgets.
I'm not saying this to earn a bride.
There are thousands I could marry.
But I will not suffer this insult from King Agamemnon.
He should have asked my permission
if he wanted to use me to lure the girl here
into his snare,
since it was to see her married to me
that Clytemnestra would have brought her most willingly.
I would have lent the use of my name
to the Greeks,
so that the ships could sail to Ilion.
I am here with the others. It is the same war.
I would not have refused to help.
But I have been treated by these commanders
as though I were nobody. They accord me their
honor or they ignore me as they please.
My sword may decide that. Blood will color it
before we sail to Phrygia

if anyone thinks to take your daughter from me.
Be calm. In your time of danger, suddenly
I appeared to you as if I were some great god.
I am not. But to save the girl,
I will be.

CHORUS: Son of Peleus, what you have said is worthy
of you, worthy of the proud sea-goddess
and her son.

CLYTEMNESTRA: How can I find the right praise,
neither cloying with flattery, nor so meager
that it offends you? Men of worth
have a way of hating those who praise them too much.
I am ashamed to enlarge on my sufferings.
They are mine, they do not concern you. Still,
even if their afflictions are not his, a good man
may help those in trouble. Take pity on us.
Our plight deserves it. First I thought
you would be my son—an empty hope, as I learned.
Now my child is threatened with death:
a bad augury for your marriage one day,
unless you take steps to protect yourself.
But why do I urge you? From beginning to end
you have spoken nobly. My child
will be saved, if you can save her. Would it please you
if she came and embraced your knees as a suppliant?
True, it is not seemly for a girl to do so,
but if you wished she would come
with dignity, and eyes cast down. And yet
if my supplication alone
can move you
I would rather she were not called.
She is over-timid, perhaps. But all forms
of modesty
are worth respecting.

ACHILLES: Do not bring your daughter
  here for me to see. Why should we incur
  the comments of the ignorant?
  An army crowded together, loosed from work at home,
  will gossip and spread foul stories.
  Whether you supplicate me or not, you come
  to the same end. For me
  the one thing of importance
  is to save you from disaster.
  And this you may count on: I never lie.
  May I die if I deceive you. And live
  only if she does.

CLYTEMNESTRA: May you be blessed all your days
  for helping those who are unhappy.

ACHILLES: We must lay plans. Listen.

CLYTEMNESTRA: Go on. I need no urging to listen to you.

ACHILLES: Let us try to make her father see reason.

CLYTEMNESTRA: He is too cowardly. He is afraid of the army.

ACHILLES: Arguments can beat down arguments.

CLYTEMNESTRA: A cold hope. But what do you want me to do?

ACHILLES: First, plead with him not to kill his daughter.
  If he refuses you, then you can come to me,
  but you may persuade him
  by yourself.
  Then there would be no need for my help.
  You are safe, in any case. And there would be
  no breach, then, in my friendship with Agamemnon,
  no cause for the army to reproach me,

no weapon used to bring it about,
only reason. So it would turn out well for you
and those dear to you
and I would not be forced to act.

CLYTEMNESTRA: How wise you are! I will do as you say. But
    suppose
something goes wrong: where
and how will I see you again?
Shall I come, in my misery, searching
for your hand to rescue us?

ACHILLES: I will be watching, in the right place.
    You will not have to be stared at
hunting through the troops to find me. Do nothing
that would disgrace your fathers.
Tyndareos should not suffer shame.
He was a great man in Greece.

CLYTEMNESTRA: You are right. Lead me. I ask only
    to be your slave.
If there are gods the gods will reward your goodness.
If there are none what does anything matter?

            (CLYTEMNESTRA *goes in at the left door,*
      the OLD MAN *at the right.* ACHILLES *goes off left.*)

CHORUS: Oh what a sound of Libyan flutes,
of lyres leading the dance, of reeling
reeds raised the marriage hymn
on Pelion, when the Muses
came robed in their bright hair to the banquet
with the gods, and their gold
sandals stamped the ground
on the way to the marriage of Peleus,
and their voices

carried over the centaurs' slopes, and through
the woods of Pelion, praise
of Thetis and Aiakos' son.
There Dardanos' child,
Trojan Ganymede, the darling of Zeus, poured out
mixed wine from the deep bowls of gold,
and in celebration the fifty
daughters of Nereus turned
their braided dance on the white sand
of the shore.
And the centaurs came
riding, with pine spears and crowned with leaves,
to the feast of the gods, and the bowl
that Bakchos filled, and they cried, "Daughter
of Nereus, great
is the son you will bear:
a light and a splendor to Thessaly,
as Cheiron, who knows
the oracles of Apollo, foretells,
saying that your child will sail with an army
of Myrmidons, and their spears, to the land of Troy
to burn King Priam's glorious city,
his limbs traced
in gold armor wrought for him
by the god Hephaistos,
the gift of his mother Thetis, the sea-goddess."
So the gods celebrated the marriage of Peleus
and the first-born of the Nereïds.
But you, Iphigeneia, on your
lovely hair the Argives will set
a wreath, as on the brows
of a spotted heifer, led down
from caves in the mountains
to the sacrifice,
and the knife will open the throat
and let the blood of a girl.

And you were not
brought up to the sound of the shepherd's pipe
and the cries of the herdsmen,
but nurtured by your mother
to be a bride for one of great Inachos' sons.
Oh where is the noble face
of modesty, or the strength of virtue, now
that blasphemy is in power
and men have put justice
behind them, and there is no law but lawlessness,
and none join in fear of the gods?

(CLYTEMNESTRA *enters from the left-hand door.*)

CLYTEMNESTRA: I have come out looking for my husband.
He has been away from here for some time. My daughter,
poor child, has learned
of the death her father plans for her.
One minute she is shaken with sobbing
and the next the tears
flow almost in silence.
But it was Agamemnon I named: here he is.
He will soon stand convicted
of planning a crime against his own child.

(AGAMEMNON *enters left, alone.*)

AGAMEMNON: Daughter of Leda, I am glad
that we meet out here,
for I must speak to you now of things that a bride
should not hear.

CLYTEMNESTRA: It's a good moment for that.

AGAMEMNON: Call the child out to her father.
The libations are ready, and the barley grains

ready to be thrown into the purifying flame,
and the calves that must loose
to Artemis their dark blood
to bless the marriage.

CLYTEMNESTRA: You find innocent words to describe it
   but there are no words
   for what you have decided. (*She calls in at the left door.*)
     Come, child.
   You know what your father means to do.
   Wrap the baby Orestes
   in your robe and bring him with you.

                (IPHIGENEIA *enters from the left door,*
         carrying ORESTES. *With her free hand she covers*
            her face with her robe. CLYTEMNESTRA *too*
             keeps her face turned from AGAMEMNON.)

Here she is, obedient to your command.
For the rest,
I will answer for us both.

AGAMEMNON: Why are you crying, child? Aren't you still
    happy
   to see me? Why are you holding your robe
   in front of your eyes,
   with your face turned to the ground?

CLYTEMNESTRA: I cannot think where
   to start my bitter story,
   for its beginning is grief,
   its middle is grief,
   its end
   is grief.

AGAMEMNON: What is it? Why are all three of you
afraid to look at me?

CLYTEMNESTRA: My husband,
find the honesty of a man
and answer me with it.

AGAMEMNON: There is no need for you to speak that way.
Ask me your question.

CLYTEMNESTRA: Do you intend to kill your daughter?

AGAMEMNON: What a horrible thing to ask! What a vile
suspicion!

CLYTEMNESTRA: Simply answer the question.

AGAMEMNON: Any reasonable question I would answer.

CLYTEMNESTRA: This question. This is the only one I care about.

AGAMEMNON: Oh immovable law of heaven! Oh my
anguish, my relentless fate!

CLYTEMNESTRA: Yours? Mine. Hers. No relenting for any of us.

AGAMEMNON: How have you been wronged?

CLYTEMNESTRA: How can you ask? What a question
for a man of sense!

AGAMEMNON (*to himself*): I am lost. Someone has betrayed me.

CLYTEMNESTRA: I know the whole story. I have found out
what you mean to do to me.

Your silence itself is a confession.
So is your sighing. No need to waste words.

AGAMEMNON: Then I will say nothing. What good would it do
    to lie, and add shamelessness to my troubles?

CLYTEMNESTRA: Listen to me, then. I will use plain words,
      and not
  talk in riddles. In the first place
  you took me by force, you married me
  against my will.
  You killed the husband I had, Tantalos.
  You ripped from my breast
  my baby, still
  living, you smashed it on the ground.
  Then when my brothers, the sons
  of Zeus, on their shining horses,
  bore down on you bringing war,
  you came on your knees to my old father
  Tyndareos, and he saved you.
  So you got me for your wife, again.
  I came to love you. Admit
  that as your wife I have deserved no reproach.
  My demands in love have been modest. I have done
  what I could to increase your house
  so that you would be glad to come home, and you went out
  proud and at peace. It is not often
  that a man acquires a good wife.
  There is no end of the other kind. And I bore you
  this son, and three daughters, and now
  you have the cruelty
  to take one of these from me.
  And if anyone asks you
  why you intend to kill her, what will you say?
  Shall I answer for you? So that Menelaos
  can have Helen back. Strange

bargain: you'll pay your child's life
as the price of a worthless woman.
We'll buy back our own harm
with what is most dear to us.
Now I want you to think of this. You'll sail
to the war, and I'll be left in the house.
You may be gone for years. There I'll be.
And with what heart, do you imagine, I will pass
my days in those halls, finding
all her places empty,
her girl's room empty of her forever, and
finding myself alone
with nothing but my tears and the endless
grieving at her fate: "My child,
it was your own father who killed you.
No one else. That was his hand,
no one else's. That was his reward for love.
And after that, he will come home again."
Then almost any occasion
would serve, for my other children and me
to give you the welcome you will have earned.
In the name of the gods, don't force me to turn
against you. Don't wrong me yourself.
As you kill our child what prayers will you be saying?
What blessing can you ask
as you have cut her throat? A bad voyage home,
since your setting out was the consequence of a crime?
And in justice, could I give you my blessing?
We would have to think the gods had no minds,
to pray for murderers.
And when you come back to Argos
will you kiss your children? It will be forbidden
by the gods. And which of the children
will dare even to look at you? They will be afraid
that you will kiss them only to kill them.
Did any of that ever cross your mind? Or do you

think of nothing but waving scepters
and leading armies? Would it not have been fair
to say to the Achaians, "Men of Argos,
you want to sail to Troy. Draw lots. Let us see
whose daughter will die." That way would have had
its justice. There is none
in offering up your daughter
as a victim for the army. Or let Menelaos,
to whom it matters most, after all, cut his own
daughter's throat: Hermione's, for the sake
of her mother. But it is my own child
who is to be torn from me, when I have been
faithful to you,
while she who dishonored her husband's bed will find
her daughter safe at home, in Sparta,
and be happy. Now answer me,
tell me if one thing I've said is not true.
But if there is justice and truth
in what I say, do not kill your daughter and mine.
Turn back, be wise.

CHORUS: Do as she asks, Agamemnon.
　　It is good when people help each other,
　　to save children. Who can deny that?

> (IPHIGENEIA *hands* ORESTES *to her mother,*
> *then kneels and clasps* AGAMEMNON'S *knees.*)

IPHIGENEIA: If I had the tongue of Orpheus, Father, whose song
　　could charm stones so that they followed after him,
　　if my words could persuade
　　whoever I wished to whatever I wished, I would use
　　all my arts now. But all that I know how to do
　　at this moment is cry. I offer you my tears.
　　I press against your knees

like a suppliant's torn branch, my body
which my mother bore you. Do not send me
into death before my time. It is sweet to see
the light. Do not make me look
at what is under the earth.
I was the first who called you father, the first
you called your child,
the first to climb on your knees, and we
held each other, we loved each other. You said,
"Will I see you living in your husband's house,
enjoying the happiness that is my daughter's right?"
And I answered, touching your beard, as I do now—
but now as the gesture
of a suppliant—"And what will I do for you
then, Father? When you are old
will you come to live with me,
and let me nurse your age, in return
for what you have done for me?"
I remember what we said, but you have forgotten.
And now you want to kill me. Oh, in the name
of Pelops, of your father
Atreus, of my mother, suffering here
again as at my birth, do not let it happen.
What have I to do with Paris
and Helen, and what they have done?
Why should Paris' coming to Argos mean that I
must die? Look at me. In my eyes. Kiss me,
so that at least I may remember that
when I am dying,
if you will not listen to what I say.

(AGAMEMNON *and* IPHIGENEIA *kiss. As she speaks the
following lines* IPHIGENEIA *takes* ORESTES
from CLYTEMNESTRA *and holds him up
to* AGAMEMNON.)

My brother, you are so small
to have to help your friends. But cry
with me, cry to your father, beg him
not to kill your sister. See,
even babies sense the dread of evil to come.
Even without being able to speak, he cries to you,
begging. Take pity on me.
Respect your daughter's life. Both of us,
your own blood, touch your beard,
imploring you: a baby,
a grown girl. In three words I can say it all:
the sweetest thing
we ever see is this daylight. Under the ground
there is nothing.
Only the mad choose to be dead. The meanest life
is better than the most glorious death.

(*She hands* ORESTES *to* CLYTEMNESTRA.)

CHORUS: Oh reckless Helen, now from you
    and your marriage
    a deadly struggle begins
    between the sons of Atreus and their children.

AGAMEMNON: I know when pity is due, and when it is not.
    I love my children. Only the mad do not.
    Wife, it is terrible to me
    to bring myself to do this,
    and terrible if I do not.
    For I am forced to do it.

(*To* IPHIGENEIA.)

Look: how many ships,
the war fleet, assembled here, the proud men of Greece
and their bronze battle-gear, and they
cannot sail to the towers
of Ilion, and seize

the famous citadel, Troy,
according to Kalchas the prophet, unless I
sacrifice you.
Some strange Aphrodite has crazed
the whole Greek army with a passion to sail at once
to the barbarians' own country
and end this piracy of Greek marriage.
If I disobey the goddess, if I ignore
the oracle, then the army will sail to Argos,
they will kill you and me, and your sisters
who are still at home. I have not become
Menelaos' creature. I am not guided by him.
It is *Greece* that compels me
to sacrifice you, whatever I wish.
We are in stronger hands than our own.
Greece must be free
if you and I can make her so. Being Greeks,
we must not be subject to barbarians,
we must not let them carry off our wives.

(*He goes off left.*)

CLYTEMNESTRA: Oh strangers, oh my daughter, now I see
your death! Your father is running away from you,
after giving you up to Hades.

IPHIGENEIA: Oh mother, how can I bear it?
The same lamenting song
falls to us both, our fate.
I must say goodbye to the light. I will not
see the sun anymore. Oh unlucky
valley of Phrygia, filled with snow,
oh high slopes of Ida where Priam
once left a baby, torn from its mother,
to die: Paris, his own child, known
in time as the son of Ida,
Paris of Ida,

among the Phrygians. If only the herdsman
had not brought him up with the flocks,
not reared him, Paris, Alexander,
to watch his flock by the clear
springs where the nymphs rise,
and the rich pastures starred
with roses and hyacinths
for the goddesses to gather.
It was there that Pallas came,
and seductive Cypris, and Hera, and with them
Hermes, the gods' messenger:
Cypris proud of the desires she wakens,
Pallas proud of her spear,
Hera proud of the bed of Zeus,
came for the fatal judgment, vying in beauty,
whose issue is my death,
oh my friends,
whatever glory it brings to the Argives.
For I am to be the first sacrifice
to Artemis for the passage to Ilion.
And he who begot me has betrayed me and left me,
and I curse in my despair,
I curse the day that ever I saw you, Helen,
for I am to be murdered, I am to fall
to my ungodly father's
ungodly knife. Oh if only
Aulis had never opened
her folded bay to the bronze-beaked galleys,
the fir keels that will ferry them to Troy,
or the breath of Zeus had not blown fair up the current
of Euripos. Sweetly he blows
on this man's sails and on that man's, making those men
happy. To others he brings
bad luck, bitter compulsion.
Some can set out on voyages, and some
can make port. Others must wait. Truly

we are creatures
of labor and suffering, and nothing for long.
Labor and suffering,
and the plain sight
of our destiny is the cruelest thing of all.

CHORUS: Oh daughter of Tyndareos, what anguish,
    what bitter sorrows
    you have called down on Greece!   (*To* IPHIGENEIA.)
    I pity you. You do not deserve your fate.

IPHIGENEIA (*looking offstage, left*): Mother, mother! I see men
    coming.

CLYTEMNESTRA (*looking in the same direction*): Achilles too,
    child, the son of the goddess,
    in whose name you were brought here.

IPHIGENEIA (*running to the left door and calling to the servants
    inside*): Women, open the doors so that I can hide.

CLYTEMNESTRA: Why, child?

IPHIGENEIA: I would be ashamed to see him.

CLYTEMNESTRA: Why?

IPHIGENEIA: I am ashamed of my unlucky marriage.

CLYTEMNESTRA: There is no time now for delicacy. Stay here.
    Do not be shy. We must do what we can.

               (*Enter* ACHILLES *left, followed by
        attendants bearing his shield, spears, sword,
             breastplate, greaves, and helmet.*)

ACHILLES: Unhappy daughter of Leda.

CLYTEMNESTRA: Unhappy is what I am.

(*Noise of shouting offstage.*)

ACHILLES: The Argives are shouting.
They want a terrible thing.

CLYTEMNESTRA: What are they shouting?

ACHILLES: About your daughter.

CLYTEMNESTRA: Your words have an unhappy beginning.

ACHILLES: They say she must be sacrificed.

CLYTEMNESTRA: And will no one speak against them?

ACHILLES: They shouted about me, too.

CLYTEMNESTRA: What did they say?

ACHILLES: "Stone him to death!"

CLYTEMNESTRA: For trying to save my daughter?

ACHILLES: For that.

CLYTEMNESTRA: Who would have dared
to raise a hand against you?

ACHILLES: Every Greek there.

CLYTEMNESTRA: But your own army of Myrmidons,
surely they took your side?

ACHILLES: They were the first to threaten me.

CLYTEMNESTRA: Oh my child, we are lost.

ACHILLES: They said I was foolish about this marriage.

CLYTEMNESTRA: What did you answer?

ACHILLES: That they were not to kill my bride.

CLYTEMNESTRA: Good.

ACHILLES: Whom her father had promised to me.

CLYTEMNESTRA: And brought here from Argos.

(*More shouting offstage, left.*)

ACHILLES: Their voices drowned me out.

CLYTEMNESTRA: The mob. An infernal thing!

ACHILLES: But I will defend you.

CLYTEMNESTRA: You alone? Against the whole army?

(ACHILLES *points to the armor-bearers.*)

ACHILLES: See. These men are carrying my armor.

CLYTEMNESTRA: May heaven reward your courage.

ACHILLES: Heaven will.

CLYTEMNESTRA: And my daughter will not be sacrificed?

ACHILLES: Not if I can stop it.

CLYTEMNESTRA: Will they come here to take the girl?

ACHILLES: Thousands of them,
   led by Odysseus.

CLYTEMNESTRA: The son of Sisyphos?

ACHILLES: That one.

CLYTEMNESTRA: Did he offer to do it, or did the army choose
   him?

ACHILLES: They chose him, but the choice pleased him.

CLYTEMNESTRA: A vile choice: to be the accomplice
   in a murder.

ACHILLES: I will stop him.

CLYTEMNESTRA: Is he going to drag her away against her will?

ACHILLES: By her blonde hair.

CLYTEMNESTRA: And what should I do then?

ACHILLES: Hold on to her.

CLYTEMNESTRA: You mean that will stop them
   from killing her?

ACHILLES: That is what it will come to.

IPHIGENEIA: Mother, both of you, listen to me.
   I see now that you are wrong

to be angry with your husband.
It is hard to hold out against the inevitable.
The stranger deserves to be thanked
for being willing to help us, but on no account
must we let the army be stirred up against him.
It would not help us, and he might come to harm.
Now mother, listen to the conclusion
that I have reached. I have made up my mind to die.
I want to come to it
with glory, I want to have thrown off
all weak and base thoughts. Mother,
look at it with my eyes,
and see how right I am.
All the people, all the strength of Greece
have turned to me. All those ships,
whether they sail, whether Troy falls,
depend on me. I will be the one
to protect our women, in the future,
if ever the barbarians dare to come near.
When they have paid for the ruin
of Helen, whom Paris carried away,
they will never again be so bold as to ravish
well-born wives out of Greece.
All these good things I can win by dying.
Because of me, Greece
will be free, and my name will be blessed there.
I must not cling to life too dearly.
You brought me into the world for the sake
of everyone in my country,
and not just for your own.
Thousands of men have slung shield on shoulder,
   thousands
have taken hold of the oars
when they saw their country wronged.
And each of them will strike and, if need be, die
for Greece. And shall my one life

stand in the way of it all?
What justice would there be in that? What answer
could I make to those who are ready to die?
There is another thing. It would not
be right for this man
to join battle with the whole of the army
and die for the sake of a woman.
If it means that one man can see the sunlight
what are the lives of thousands of women
in the balance? And if Artemis
demands the offering of my body,
I am a mortal: who am I
to oppose the goddess? It is not to be
considered. I give my life to Greece.
Take me, kill me,
and bring down Troy. That will be my monument
for ages to come. That will be my wedding,
my children, the meaning of my life.
Mother, it is the Greeks
who must rule the barbarians,
not the barbarians the Greeks.
They are born to be slaves; we
to be free.

CHORUS: Young woman, what you have said is noble.
It is the role of destiny, in this,
and the role of the goddess,
that are sick.

ACHILLES: Daughter of Agamemnon, if I could win you
for my wife, it would prove that some god
wanted to make me happy. I envy
Greece because you are hers, and you
because she is yours. What you have said
is beautiful, and worthy
of your country. You are no match

for the gods, and you have given up
the struggle against them. You have reconciled
what should be with what must be.
But as for me, the more clearly I see your spirit
the more I long to have
so noble a woman for my bride. Look. I want
to save you. To take you home with me.
I call Thetis my mother to witness: now more
than anything it would grieve me
not to pit myself against all the Danaans
and save you.
Think. Death is awesome. Something terrible.

IPHIGENEIA: I say what I am about to say
with no regard for anyone.
Tyndareos' daughter,
Helen, will bring on enough fighting, enough
death, for the sake of her body. As for you, stranger,
do not die for me,
and do not kill.
Let me save Greece if that is what I can do.

ACHILLES: Oh noble spirit! After that
what is there for me to say? You have chosen.
A splendor in your soul has led you—
why should a man not say it?
But later you may think differently. I want you
to know how I keep my word. I will have these arms
lying by the altar, ready
not to join in your death but to prevent it.
Even when the knife is almost at your neck
it will not be too late to accept my offer.
Turn, and I will not let you die
because of a moment's recklessness.
I will go now to the goddess's temple, with these arms,
and wait there until you come.

(ACHILLES *goes off, left,
followed by his armor-bearers.*)

IPHIGENEIA: You are silent. But the tears keep falling.
Mother, why these tears for me?

CLYTEMNESTRA: I have reason enough, with this ache in my
heart.

IPHIGENEIA: No more of that. Do not take
my own courage from me.
Will you do one thing for me?

CLYTEMNESTRA: Speak. How could I fail you in anything, child?

IPHIGENEIA: Do not cut off a lock of your hair
as is done for the dead.
Put on no mourning for me.

CLYTEMNESTRA: What do you mean, child? I am losing you . . .

IPHIGENEIA: No. I am saved. My name will be your glory.

CLYTEMNESTRA: I don't understand. I am not to mourn for you?

IPHIGENEIA: No. I shall have no grave.

CLYTEMNESTRA: What of that? It is not the grave we mourn,
but the dead.

IPHIGENEIA: The altar of the goddess, the daughter of Zeus,
will be my grave. Tears are forbidden there.

CLYTEMNESTRA: My daughter, what you say is true.
I will obey you.

IPHIGENEIA: For I am blessed by fortune. It was I
   who could bring help to Greece.

CLYTEMNESTRA: And what shall I say to your sisters?

IPHIGENEIA: Do not dress them in mourning either.

CLYTEMNESTRA: Have you some message of love to send them?

IPHIGENEIA: Say goodbye to them for me. And bring up
   Orestes to be a man
   for my sake.

CLYTEMNESTRA (*holding* ORESTES *up to* IPHIGENEIA): Put your
      arms around him
   since you are looking at him for the last time.

IPHIGENEIA (*hugging him*): Dear child, you did what you could
      for those you love.

CLYTEMNESTRA: Is there something I can do in Argos,
   something that would give you pleasure?

IPHIGENEIA: Don't hate my father. He is your husband.

CLYTEMNESTRA: He will not like the course he must face
      because of you.

IPHIGENEIA: He destroyed me for the sake of Greece
   against his will.

CLYTEMNESTRA: But he used lies,
   low schemes unworthy of Atreus.

IPHIGENEIA: Who will lead me to the place
   so that they don't need to touch my hair?

CLYTEMNESTRA: I will go with you . . .

IPHIGENEIA (*interrupting*): No. That would not be right.

CLYTEMNESTRA: . . . holding on to your gown.

IPHIGENEIA: Mother, listen to me. It is better for both of us
    if you stay here. One of my father's
    servants here can lead me to the meadow
    where I am to be killed.

> (*An attendant comes forward and
> takes* IPHIGENEIA'S *hand.*)

CLYTEMNESTRA: My child, you are going . . .

IPHIGENEIA: And I shall never come back.

CLYTEMNESTRA: Leaving your mother.

IPHIGENEIA: As you see. Not because I deserve it.

CLYTEMNESTRA: Wait. Do not leave me . . .

IPHIGENEIA: Now there must be no tears.
    And you, young women,
    join in my hymn to Artemis the virgin,
    and celebrate my fate.
    Let silence
    descend on the army of the Argives.
    Let the basket be brought,
    light the fire of purification,
    bring the barley. Father
    must lead the procession around the altar.
    I am coming bringing salvation for Greece,
    and victory. Lead me.

(*The attendant begins to lead* IPHIGENEIA *offstage
left while she sings her triumphant lament.*)

I who will conquer Troy
and bring down the city of Ilion.
Set the wreath on my head.
Bring the purifying waters.
Around the temple of Artemis, around
the altar of blessed Artemis,
in honor of the goddess begin
the dance. I will wash away
with my own blood the spell
that the oracle revealed.

CHORUS: Oh noble and revered mother,
  we may not shed our tears for you.
  The gods are not worshipped that way.

IPHIGENEIA: Young women, sing with me now
  glory to Artemis the goddess
  whose temple faces Chalkis
  where the ships wait, and
  the passion for war is burning,
  here in the narrows of Aulis,
  because of me. Oh Pelasgia where I was born,
  Mycenae,
  home!

CHORUS: Are you invoking the city of Perseus
  which the Cyclopes built?

IPHIGENEIA: You brought me up
  to be the light of Greece.
  Dying, I can say it.

CHORUS: Your glory will not die.

IPHIGENEIA: Oh light that brings the day, splendor
   of Zeus, I am going
   from this world to another destiny,
   another home. Goodbye
   light that I love.

>   (*She goes out left, singing.* CLYTEMNESTRA *carries*
>   ORESTES *inside the left door of the tent.*)

CHORUS: See, she is going. She who will conquer
   Troy and bring down the city of Ilion.
   She leans her head for the victim's garland,
   for the sacred water. She goes
   to drench with her blood the altar
   of the divine goddess,
   to the sword that will cut
   her lovely throat. Your father is waiting
   with the pure libations, and the Achaians
   are waiting to sail to Troy.
   But let us raise our voices to Artemis, daughter
   of Zeus, to ask
   for a happy destiny. Awesome goddess,
   pleased by this human sacrifice, send now
   to Phrygia, to the land of deceitful Troy,
   the armies of Greece.
   There let Agamemnon
   wreathe the Achaian weapons with garlands
   of victory, and himself win
   a crown of unfading glory.

MESSENGER (*enters left and calls at the left door*): Daughter of
   Tyndareos, Clytemnestra,
   come out and hear my message.

CLYTEMNESTRA (*enters, carrying* ORESTES): I heard your voice.
   Here I am,
   distraught, shaking with terror,
   for fear that you have brought some new disaster
   to add to the grief I have.

MESSENGER: It is about your daughter. I have
   something miraculous to tell.

CLYTEMNESTRA: Tell me, tell me at once.

MESSENGER: Beloved mistress, you shall hear everything
   as it happened, from the beginning,
   unless the seething of my mind
   confuses my words. When we had come to the grove
   sacred to the daughter of Zeus,
   and the flowered meadow of Artemis,
   leading your child
   to the place where the army
   was ordered to assemble,
   the Argives ran, all crowding to the spot.
   And King Agamemnon, when he saw his daughter
   coming through the grove to the place of sacrifice,
   groaned aloud and turned his head, hiding
   his eyes and their tears with his robe.
   But she came up to her father and said, "Father,
   here I am. And I give my body
   willingly as a sacrifice
   for my country, for all of Greece.
   Lead me to the altar
   if this is what destiny has decreed.
   For my part, I hope
   it turns out well for all of you.
   May the spoils of victory be yours,

and then the sight of your homes again.
Let none of the Argives lay hands on me.
I will offer my neck in silence,
I will not flinch." That is what she said,
and everyone who heard marvelled
at the girl's bravery and nobility.
Then the herald Talthybios, whose office it was,
called out from among them, to the army,
for the sacred silence,
and the prophet Kalchas drew from its sheath
the whetted knife, and laid it
in the basket worked with gold,
and set the crown upon her head. And Peleus' son
took the basket and the lustral water
and circled the altar, calling out,
"Daughter of Zeus, who bring death
to the wild creatures, who turn
your gleaming star through the darkness, accept
this sacrifice offered to you by us, the army
of the Achaians, and King Agamemnon,
this pure blood
from the throat of a beautiful girl. Now let our
war fleet embark on a smooth voyage
and our weapons bring down the walls of Troy."
Then the sons of Atreus and the whole army stood
with their eyes fixed on the ground, and the priest
took up the knife,
praying, and looked for the place
to plunge it. Pain welled up in me
at that, and I dropped my eyes.
And the miracle happened. Everyone
distinctly heard the sound of the knife
striking, but no one could see
the girl. She had vanished.
The priest cried out, and the whole army
echoed him, seeing

what some god had sent, a thing
nobody could have prophesied. There it was,
we could see it, but we could scarcely
believe it: a deer
lay there gasping, a large,
beautiful animal, and its blood ran
streaming over the altar of the goddess.
Then Kalchas, with
such joy as you can imagine, shouted, "Commanders
of the assembled armies of Greece, look:
the goddess has placed this victim
on her altar, a deer from the mountains,
and she accepts this instead of the girl,
rather than stain her altar with noble blood.
With this she is happy, and now she blesses
our voyage to attack Ilion.
Therefore everyone who is to sail
take heart and go down to his ship,
for today we must leave the hollow gulf of Aulis,
and cross the Aegean Sea."
Then when Hephaistos' flame had left nothing
of the victim but ashes, he offered
the customary prayer for the army's safe return.
Agamemnon sent me to say this,
to tell you of this
destiny which the gods have sent
and of the glory which he has won
among the Greeks. I saw it myself. I was there.
It is plain that your daughter
has been taken up into heaven.
Let this quiet your grief
and put an end to your anger against your husband.
No man living can tell what the gods will do,
but they save those whom they love.
This same day has seen
your daughter dead and brought to life again.

CHORUS: With what joy for your sake
I hear the messenger's words! Showing
how the girl is alive in heaven with the gods.

CLYTEMNESTRA: Oh child, what deity has carried you off?
How may I address you? How can I be sure,
how can I know,
that this is not all a lie, made up
to silence my bitter grieving?

CHORUS: Here comes King Agamemnon. He will tell you
the same thing.

(AGAMEMNON *enters left, attended by generals,*
priests with the paraphernalia of sacrifice,
soldiers, camp-followers, sailors, and others
taking part in the expedition to Troy.)

AGAMEMNON: Lady, as for your daughter,
we have reason to be happy. For truly
she has the gods for company.
Now you must take this young calf here (*indicates* ORESTES)
and travel home. The army is preparing to sail.
Goodbye. My greetings will be slow
in reaching you from Troy. May you be happy.

CHORUS: Son of Atreus, sail
with a light heart to the land of Phrygia,
and return with a light heart
and heavy spoils
from Troy.

(AGAMEMNON, *generals, etc., go off left, followed by*
the CHORUS. CLYTEMNESTRA, *carrying* ORESTES,
goes in the main door of the tent.
She does not look back.) ∿

Interpretive Questions
for Discussion

Does Iphigeneia agree to die because she wants to be the savior of Greece or because she wants to rescue her father?

1. In seeing herself as the savior of Greece, is Iphigeneia embracing the idea that "humility is wisdom," or is she pursuing glory as tenaciously as her father, Achilles, and the other Greek heroes? (120)

2. In accepting her death, is Iphigeneia demonstrating the virtue of a woman—showing "a stillness" in her love—or that of a man, which "makes a city great"? (120)

3. Why does Clytemnestra tell Iphigeneia about Agamemnon's treachery before she pleads the case for Iphigeneia's life with him? (147)

4. Why does the Chorus of Chalkidian women say that at Aulis "blasphemy is in power" and "there is no law but lawlessness, and none join in fear of the gods"? (147) Are we meant to think that a Chorus of Chalkidian *men* might not see things this way?

5. If Iphigeneia believes that she doesn't deserve to die, why does she tell her mother not to mourn her death? (164–165)

6. Why does Iphigeneia urge her mother not to hate her husband? Why does Iphigeneia insist that Agamemnon ordered her sacrifice against his will? (160, 165)

7. Why does Euripides have the Chorus say that Iphigeneia is noble and that the roles of destiny and Artemis are "sick"? Why does Achilles think that Iphigeneia is "no match for the gods"? (162–163)

8. Does Achilles speak for Euripides when he says that it is noble to reconcile "what should be with what must be"? (163)

9. Does Euripides intend for us to believe that the Greeks are the free people they claim they are? (cf. 155, 162)

10. Why does Iphigeneia change from believing that, "Only the mad choose to be dead. The meanest life is better than the most glorious death," to believing that she is "blessed by fortune"? (154, 165)

Suggested textual analysis
Pages 160–163: beginning, "IPHIGENEIA: Mother, both of you, listen to me," and ending, "and wait there until you come."

Why does Agamemnon sacrifice his daughter to fight for a morally empty cause?

1. Why can't Agamemnon remain steadfast in his decision not to sacrifice his daughter? Why is he unable to reconcile the demands of morality and politics?

2. Is the sacrifice of his daughter a just test of Agamemnon's leadership? Why is Artemis said to demand that Agamemnon give her the life of Iphigeneia, the child who loves him the most?

3. Why does Agamemnon say that when Menelaos began "reasoning" with him, he was persuaded to lure his beloved daughter to her death? (100) Why does Agamemnon claim that being forced to choose between his child and his command has made him lose the use of his reason? (101)

4. Is Agamemnon as much a victim of fate as Iphigeneia? (115)

5. Why does Agamemnon see himself as the slave of the mob he leads? Why does Menelaos, a king himself, tell Agamemnon that he is "wrong to go in such dread of the mob"? (115, 118)

6. Why does Agamemnon say that Menelaos has "won" even though Menelaos withdraws his demand for Iphigeneia's life immediately after their argument? Why is Menelaos surprised when Agamemnon claims that he is "forced" to kill his daughter? (116–117)

7. Why does Agamemnon claim that Argos would be threatened by his refusal to sacrifice Iphigeneia? Is he making excuses, or does he rightly perceive that the Greeks' fever for war is so high that they would turn on his kingdom if they couldn't fight Troy? (119, 154–155)

8. Why won't Agamemnon, unlike Clytemnestra, risk his life to save his child?

9. Why must Agamemnon agree to sacrifice his daughter—an "ungodly" and barbaric act—in order to make Greece free of barbarian subjugation? (155–157)

10. Are we meant to think that Iphigeneia's tragedy is caused by a failure of leadership or by the caprice of the gods? (cf. 109–111, 155–156)

Suggested textual analyses

Pages 108–111: beginning, "MENELAOS: How do you feel about a mind," and ending, "A general needs to have a mind."

Pages 114–117: beginning, "Oh miserable creature that I am," and ending, "to kill my daughter."

Why do the fates weave the death of the virgin Iphigeneia into the homecoming of the unfaithful Queen Helen?

1. Why are the Greeks in a "frenzy" to fight a war to bring back the faithless wife of Menelaos? (133)

2. Why do both the Chorus and Agamemnon link sexual passion to the passion for war? (103–104, 112, 154) Why do the young women of the Chorus acknowledge their excitement at seeing the Greek heroes, but later pray to "know love within reason, and desire within marriage"? (103–104, 120)

3. Why does Euripides make the promise of marriage to the warrior Achilles the pretext for luring Iphigeneia to Aulis?

4. Why does Iphigeneia say that it would not be right for Achilles to die for the sake of a woman, even though this is what the Trojan War is all about? (161) Are we meant to think that she has fallen in love with Achilles and is sacrificing herself for his sake?

5. Why does Agamemnon accuse Menelaos of wanting the war because he is "pining for a virtuous wife"? (111)

6. Why does the Chorus of Chalkidian women imagine the women of Troy lamenting their inevitable abduction and blaming Helen—who is herself an offspring of a rape by Zeus of her mother, Leda? (132–133)

7. Why does Clytemnestra begin her plea for Iphigeneia's life by reminding Agamemnon that he took her by force, brutally murdering her first husband and her child by him? (150)

8. Why does Clytemnestra try to persuade Agamemnon not to sacrifice Iphigeneia by saying that doing so will turn her into a faithless wife, like Helen? Why does she appeal to his pride as a man and a husband, rather than to his fatherly affections? (151–152)

9. Does Achilles agree to defend Iphigeneia because it is the reasonable and just thing to do or because his pride has been injured? (139, 141–143) Why does Achilles end up participating in Iphigeneia's sacrifice even though he had sworn he would not? (163, 170)

10. Why does Euripides make Iphigeneia disappear, replaced by a beautiful deer that is sacrificed in her place? Why does Euripides have Clytemnestra question whether this story is true? (171–172)

Suggested textual analysis
Pages 120–121: beginning, "CHORUS: Blessed are they," and ending, "to sack Troy."

FOR FURTHER REFLECTION

1. In the context of the play, can the sacrifice of Iphigeneia be seen as a civilized act? Why, unlike in the story of Abraham and Isaac, is Iphigeneia not restored to her family?

2. Are men more likely than women to follow the urges of ambition when ambition conflicts with the duties of parenthood? Does the "mystery" of giving birth mean that mothers value their children's lives more than fathers do?

3. Are men like Agamemnon "ungodly" and unnatural, or do the responsibilities of great leadership create impossible demands that have no parallels for the common man?

4. When parents send their children to war, are they showing a willingness to make a sacrifice similar to Agamemnon's?

5. Does a noble action in a wrong cause deserve glory? Does Iphigeneia achieve nobility for accepting her undeserved death instead of denouncing it and its cause—a war to recapture a faithless woman?

6. Is it noble or merely pragmatic to reconcile "what should be with what must be"? (162)

7. If women ran the world, would there be no more wars?

BARN BURNING

William Faulkner

WILLIAM FAULKNER (1897–1962)
was awarded the Nobel Prize for literature
in 1949 "for his powerful and artistically
independent contribution to the new
American novel." An intensely private writer
who spent almost his entire life in Oxford,
Mississippi, Faulkner set most of his tales in
Yoknapatawpha County, Mississippi, a place
that existed solely in the author's imagination. Faulkner's stories and novels, often
characterized by the use of interior mono-
logue, are peopled by many recurring
characters—declining Southern aristocrats,
blacks, and poor whites—from families
spanning several generations. Faulkner's
Snopes trilogy—*The Hamlet* (1940),
The Town (1957), and *The Mansion*
(1959)—traces the rise of one such family.

T HE STORE in which the Justice of the Peace's court was sitting smelled of cheese. The boy, crouched on his nail keg at the back of the crowded room, knew he smelled cheese, and more: from where he sat he could see the ranked shelves close-packed with the solid, squat, dynamic shapes of tin cans whose labels his stomach read, not from the lettering which meant nothing to his mind but from the scarlet devils and the silver curve of fish—this, the cheese which he knew he smelled and the hermetic meat which his intestines believed he smelled coming in intermittent gusts momentary and brief between the other constant one, the smell and sense just a little of fear because mostly of despair and grief, the old fierce pull of blood. He could not see the table where the Justice sat and before which his father and his father's enemy (*our enemy* he thought in that despair; *ourn! mine and hisn both! He's my father!*) stood, but he could hear them, the two of them that is, because his father had said no word yet:

"But what proof have you, Mr. Harris?"

"I told you. The hog got into my corn. I caught it up and sent it back to him. He had no fence that would hold it. I told him so, warned him. The next time I put the hog in my pen. When he came to get it I gave him enough wire to patch up his pen. The next time I put the hog up and kept it. I rode down to his house and saw the wire I gave him still rolled on to the spool in his yard. I told him he could have the hog when he paid me a dollar pound fee. That evening a nigger came with the dollar and got the hog. He was a strange nigger. He said, 'He say to tell you wood and hay kin burn.' I said, 'What?' 'That whut he say to tell you,' the nigger said. 'Wood and hay kin burn.' That night my barn burned. I got the stock out but I lost the barn."

"Where is the nigger? Have you got him?"

"He was a strange nigger, I tell you. I don't know what became of him."

"But that's not proof. Don't you see that's not proof?"

"Get that boy up here. He knows." For a moment the boy thought too that the man meant his older brother until Harris said, "Not him. The little one. The boy," and, crouching, small for his age, small and wiry like his father, in patched and faded jeans even too small for him, with straight, uncombed, brown hair and eyes gray and wild as storm scud, he saw the men between himself and the table part and become a lane of grim faces, at the end of which he saw the Justice, a shabby, collarless, graying man in spectacles, beckoning him. He felt no floor under his bare feet; he seemed to walk beneath the palpable weight of the grim turning faces. His father, stiff in his black Sunday coat donned not for the trial but for the moving, did not even look at him. *He aims for me to lie,* he thought, again with that frantic grief and despair. *And I will have to do hit.*

"What's your name, boy?" the Justice said.

"Colonel Sartoris Snopes," the boy whispered.

"Hey?" the Justice said. "Talk louder. Colonel Sartoris? I reckon anybody named for Colonel Sartoris in this country can't help but tell the truth, can they?" The boy said nothing. *Enemy! Enemy!* he thought; for a moment he could not even see, could not see that the Justice's face was kindly nor discern that his voice was troubled when he spoke to the man named Harris: "Do you want me to question this boy?" But he could hear, and during those subsequent long seconds while there was absolutely no sound in the crowded little room save that of quiet and intent breathing it was as if he had swung outward at the end of a grapevine, over a ravine, and at the top of the swing had been caught in a prolonged instant of mesmerized gravity, weightless in time.

"No!" Harris said violently, explosively. "Damnation! Send him out of here!" Now time, the fluid world, rushed beneath him again, the voices coming to him again through the smell of cheese and sealed meat, the fear and despair and the old grief of blood:

"This case is closed. I can't find against you, Snopes, but I can give you advice. Leave this country and don't come back to it."

His father spoke for the first time, his voice cold and harsh, level, without emphasis: "I aim to. I don't figure to stay in a country among people who . . ." he said something unprintable and vile, addressed to no one.

"That'll do," the Justice said. "Take your wagon and get out of this country before dark. Case dismissed."

His father turned, and he followed the stiff black coat, the wiry figure walking a little stiffly from where a Confederate provost's man's musket ball had taken him in the heel on a stolen horse thirty years ago, followed the two backs now, since his older brother had appeared from somewhere in the crowd, no taller than the father but thicker, chewing tobacco steadily, between the two lines of grim-faced men and out of the store and across the worn gallery and down the sagging steps and among the dogs and half-grown boys in the mild May dust, where as he passed a voice hissed:

"Barn burner!"

Again he could not see, whirling; there was a face in a red haze, moonlike, bigger than the full moon, the owner of it half again his size, he leaping in the red haze toward the face, feeling no blow, feeling no shock when his head struck the earth, scrabbling up and leaping again, feeling no blow this time either and tasting no blood, scrabbling up to see the other boy in full flight and himself already leaping into pursuit as his father's hand jerked him back, the harsh, cold voice speaking above him: "Go get in the wagon."

It stood in a grove of locusts and mulberries across the road. His two hulking sisters in their Sunday dresses and his mother and her sister in calico and sunbonnets were already in it, sitting on and among the sorry residue of the dozen and more movings which even the boy could remember—the battered stove, the broken beds and chairs, the clock inlaid with mother-of-pearl, which would not run, stopped at some fourteen minutes past two o'clock of a dead and forgotten day and time, which had been his mother's dowry. She was crying, though when she saw him she drew her sleeve across her face and began to descend from the wagon. "Get back," the father said.

"He's hurt. I got to get some water and wash his . . ."

"Get back in the wagon," his father said. He got in too, over the tailgate. His father mounted to the seat where the older brother already sat and struck the gaunt mules two savage blows with the peeled willow, but without heat. It was not even sadistic; it was exactly that same quality which in later years would cause his descendants to over-run the engine before putting a motor car into motion, striking and reining back in the same movement. The wagon went on, the store with its quiet crowd of grimly watching men dropped behind; a curve in the road hid it. *Forever* he thought. *Maybe he's done satisfied now, now that he has* . . . stopping himself, not to say it aloud even to himself. His mother's hand touched his shoulder.

"Does hit hurt?" she said.

"Naw," he said. "Hit don't hurt. Lemme be."

"Can't you wipe some of the blood off before hit dries?"

"I'll wash tonight," he said. "Lemme be, I tell you."

The wagon went on. He did not know where they were going. None of them ever did or ever asked, because it was always somewhere, always a house of sorts waiting for them a day or two days or even three days away. Likely his father had already arranged to make a crop on another farm before he . . . Again he had to stop himself. He (the father) always did. There was something about his wolflike independence and even courage when the advantage was at least neutral which impressed strangers, as if they got from his latent ravening ferocity not so much a sense of dependability as a feeling that his ferocious conviction in the rightness of his own actions would be of advantage to all whose interest lay with his.

That night they camped in a grove of oaks and beeches where a spring ran. The nights were still cool and they had a fire against it, of a rail lifted from a nearby fence and cut into lengths—a small fire, neat, niggard almost, a shrewd fire; such fires were his father's habit and custom always, even in freezing weather. Older, the boy might have remarked this and wondered why not a big one; why should not a man who had not only seen the waste and extravagance of war, but who had in his blood an inherent voracious prodigality with material not his own, have burned everything in sight? Then he might have gone a step farther and thought that that was the reason: that niggard blaze was the living fruit of nights passed during those four years in the woods hiding from all men, blue or gray, with his strings of horses (captured horses, he called them). And older still, he might have divined the true reason: that the element of fire spoke to some deep mainspring of his father's being, as the element of steel or of powder spoke to other men, as the one weapon for the preservation of integrity, else breath were not worth the breathing, and hence to be regarded with respect and used with discretion.

But he did not think this now and he had seen those same niggard blazes all his life. He merely ate his supper beside it and was already half asleep over his iron plate when his father called him, and once more he followed the stiff back, the stiff and ruthless limp, up the slope and on to the starlit road where, turning, he could see his father against the stars but without face or depth—a shape black, flat, and bloodless as though cut from tin in the iron folds of the frockcoat which had not been made for him, the voice harsh like tin and without heat like tin:

"You were fixing to tell them. You would have told him." He didn't answer. His father struck him with the flat of his hand on the side of the head, hard but without heat, exactly as he had struck the two mules at the store, exactly as he would strike either of them with any stick in order to kill a horse fly, his voice still without heat or anger: "You're getting to be a man. You got to learn. You got to learn to stick to your own blood or you ain't going to have any blood to stick to you. Do you think either of them, any man there this morning, would? Don't you know all they wanted was a chance to get at me because they knew I had them beat? Eh?" Later, twenty years later, he was to tell himself, "If I had said they wanted only truth, justice, he would have hit me again." But now he said nothing. He was not crying. He just stood there. "Answer me," his father said.

"Yes," he whispered. His father turned.

"Get on to bed. We'll be there tomorrow."

Tomorrow they were there. In the early afternoon the wagon stopped before a paintless two-room house identical almost with the dozen others it had stopped before even in the boy's ten years, and again, as on the other dozen occasions, his mother and aunt got down and began to unload the wagon, although his two sisters and his father and brother had not moved.

"Likely hit ain't fitten for hawgs," one of the sisters said.

"Nevertheless, fit it will and you'll hog it and like it," his father said. "Get out of them chairs and help your Ma unload."

The two sisters got down, big, bovine, in a flutter of cheap ribbons; one of them drew from the jumbled wagon bed a battered lantern, the other a worn broom. His father handed the reins to the older son and began to climb stiffly over the wheel. "When they get unloaded, take the team to the barn and feed them." Then he said, and at first the boy thought he was still speaking to his brother: "Come with me."

"Me?" he said.

"Yes," his father said. "You."

"Abner," his mother said. His father paused and looked back—the harsh level stare beneath the shaggy, graying, irascible brows.

"I reckon I'll have a word with the man that aims to begin tomorrow owning me body and soul for the next eight months."

They went back up the road. A week ago—or before last night, that is—he would have asked where they were going, but not now. His father had struck him before last night but never before had he paused afterward to explain why; it was as if the blow and the following calm, outrageous voice still rang, repercussed, divulging nothing to him save the terrible handicap of being young, the light weight of his few years, just heavy enough to prevent his soaring free of the world as it seemed to be ordered but not heavy enough to keep him footed solid in it, to resist it and try to change the course of its events.

Presently he could see the grove of oaks and cedars and the other flowering trees and shrubs where the house would be, though not the house yet. They walked beside a fence massed with honeysuckle and Cherokee roses and came to a gate swinging open between two brick pillars, and now, beyond a sweep of drive, he saw the house for the first time and at that instant he forgot his father and the terror and despair both, and even when he remembered his father again (who had not stopped) the terror and despair did not return. Because, for all the twelve movings, they had sojourned until now in a poor country, a land of small farms and fields and houses, and he had never seen a house like this before. *Hit's big as a courthouse* he thought quietly, with a surge of peace and joy whose reason he could not have thought into words, being too young for that: *They are safe from him. People whose lives are a part of this peace and dignity are beyond his touch, he no more to them than a buzzing wasp: capable of stinging for a little moment but that's all; the spell of this peace and dignity rendering even the barns and stable and cribs which belong to it impervious to the puny flames he might contrive* . . . this, the peace and joy, ebbing for an instant as he looked again at the stiff black back, the stiff and implacable limp of the figure which was not dwarfed by the house, for the reason that it had never looked big anywhere and which now, against the serene columned backdrop, had more than ever that impervious quality of something cut ruthlessly from tin, depthless, as though, sidewise to the sun, it would cast no shadow. Watching him, the boy remarked the absolutely undeviating course which his father held and saw the stiff foot come squarely down in a pile of fresh droppings where a horse had stood in the drive and which his father could have avoided by a simple change of stride. But it ebbed only for a moment, though he could not have thought this into words either, walking on in the spell of the house, which he could even want but without envy, without sorrow, certainly never with that ravening and jealous rage which unknown to him walked in the ironlike black coat before him: *Maybe he will feel it too. Maybe it will even change him now from what maybe he couldn't help but be.*

They crossed the portico. Now he could hear his father's stiff foot as it came down on the boards with clocklike finality, a sound out of all proportion to the displacement of the body it bore and which was not dwarfed either by the white door before it, as though it had attained to a sort of vicious and ravening minimum not to be dwarfed by anything—the flat, wide, black hat, the formal coat of broadcloth which had once been black but which had now that friction-glazed greenish cast of the bodies of old house flies, the lifted sleeve which was too large, the lifted hand like a curled claw. The door opened so promptly that the boy knew the Negro must have been watching them all the time, an old man with neat grizzled hair, in a linen jacket, who stood barring the door with his body, saying, "Wipe yo foots, white man, fo you come in here. Major ain't home nohow."

"Get out of my way, nigger," his father said, without heat too, flinging the door back and the Negro also and entering, his hat still on his head. And now the boy saw the prints of the stiff foot on the doorjamb and saw them appear on the pale rug behind the machinelike deliberation of the foot which seemed to bear (or transmit) twice the weight which the body compassed. The Negro was shouting "Miss Lula! Miss Lula!" somewhere behind them, then the boy, deluged as though by a warm wave by a suave turn of carpeted stair and a pendant glitter of chandeliers and a mute gleam of gold frames, heard the swift feet and saw her too, a lady—perhaps he had never seen her like before either—in a gray, smooth gown with lace at the throat and an apron tied at the waist and the sleeves turned back, wiping cake or biscuit dough from her hands with a towel as she came up the hall, looking not at his father at all but at the tracks on the blond rug with an expression of incredulous amazement.

"I tried," the Negro cried. "I tole him to . . ."

"Will you please go away?" she said in a shaking voice. "Major de Spain is not at home. Will you please go away?"

His father had not spoken again. He did not speak again. He did not even look at her. He just stood stiff in the center of the rug, in his hat, the shaggy iron-gray brows twitching slightly above the pebble-colored eyes as he appeared to examine the house with brief deliberation. Then with the same deliberation he turned; the boy watched him pivot on the good leg and saw the stiff foot drag round the arc of the turning, leaving a final long and fading smear. His father never looked at it, he never once looked down at the rug. The Negro held the door. It closed behind them, upon the hysteric and indistinguishable woman-wail. His father stopped at the top of the steps and scraped his boot clean on the edge of it. At the gate he stopped again. He stood for a moment, planted stiffly on the stiff foot, looking back at the house. "Pretty and white, ain't it?" he said. "That's sweat. Nigger sweat. Maybe it ain't white enough yet to suit him. Maybe he wants to mix some white sweat with it."

Two hours later the boy was chopping wood behind the house within which his mother and aunt and the two sisters (the mother and aunt, not the two girls, he knew that; even at this distance and muffled by walls the flat loud voices of the two girls emanated an incorrigible idle inertia) were setting up the stove to prepare a meal, when he heard the hooves and saw the linen-clad man on a fine sorrel mare, whom he recognized even before he saw the rolled rug in front of the Negro youth following on a fat bay carriage horse—a suffused, angry face vanishing, still at full gallop, beyond the corner of the house where his father and brother were sitting in the two tilted chairs; and a moment later, almost before he could have put the axe down, he heard the hooves again and watched the sorrel mare go back out of the yard, already galloping again. Then his father began to shout one of the sisters' names, who presently emerged backward from the kitchen door dragging the rolled rug along the ground by one end while the other sister walked behind it.

"If you ain't going to tote, go on and set up the wash pot," the first said.

"You, Sarty!" the second shouted. "Set up the wash pot!" His father appeared at the door, framed against that shabbiness, as he had been against that other bland perfection, impervious to either, the mother's anxious face at his shoulder.

"Go on," the father said. "Pick it up." The two sisters stooped, broad, lethargic; stooping, they presented an incredible expanse of pale cloth and a flutter of tawdry ribbons.

"If I thought enough of a rug to have to git hit all the way from France I wouldn't keep hit where folks coming in would have to tromp on hit," the first said. They raised the rug.

"Abner," the mother said. "Let me do it."

"You go back and git dinner," his father said. "I'll tend to this."

From the woodpile through the rest of the afternoon the boy watched them, the rug spread flat in the dust beside the bubbling wash pot, the two sisters stooping over it with that profound and lethargic reluctance, while the father stood over them in turn, implacable and grim, driving them though never raising his voice again. He could smell the harsh homemade lye they were using; he saw his mother come to the door once and look toward them with an expression not anxious now but very

like despair; he saw his father turn, and he fell to with the axe
and saw from the corner of his eye his father raise from the
ground a flattish fragment of fieldstone and examine it and
return to the pot, and this time his mother actually spoke:
"Abner. Abner. Please don't. Please, Abner."

Then he was done too. It was dusk; the whippoorwills had
already begun. He could smell coffee from the room where they
would presently eat the cold food remaining from the mid-after-
noon meal, though when he entered the house he realized they
were having coffee again probably because there was a fire on
the hearth, before which the rug now lay spread over the backs
of the two chairs. The tracks of his father's foot were gone.
Where they had been were now long, water-cloudy scoriations
resembling the sporadic course of a lilliputian mowing machine.

It still hung there while they ate the cold food and then went
to bed, scattered without order or claim up and down the two
rooms, his mother in one bed, where his father would later lie,
the older brother in the other, himself, the aunt, and the two sisters on pallets on the floor. But his father was not in bed yet.
The last thing the boy remembered was the depthless, harsh silhouette of the hat and coat bending over the rug and it seemed
to him that he had not even closed his eyes when the silhouette
was standing over him, the fire almost dead behind it, the stiff
foot prodding him awake. "Catch up the mule," his father said.

When he returned with the mule his father was standing in
the black door, the rolled rug over his shoulder. "Ain't you
going to ride?" he said.

"No. Give me your foot."

He bent his knee into his father's hand, the wiry, surprising
power flowed smoothly, rising, he rising with it, on to the mule's
bare back (they had owned a saddle once; the boy could remember it though not when or where) and with the same
effortlessness his father swung the rug up in front of him. Now
in the starlight they retraced the afternoon's path, up the dusty
road rife with honeysuckle, through the gate and up the black
tunnel of the drive to the lightless house, where he sat on the

mule and felt the rough warp of the rug drag across his thighs and vanish.

"Don't you want me to help?" he whispered. His father did not answer and now he heard again that stiff foot striking the hollow portico with that wooden and clocklike deliberation, that outrageous overstatement of the weight it carried. The rug, hunched, not flung (the boy could tell that even in the darkness) from his father's shoulder struck the angle of wall and floor with a sound unbelievably loud, thunderous, then the foot again, unhurried and enormous; a light came on in the house and the boy sat, tense, breathing steadily and quietly and just a little fast, though the foot itself did not increase its beat at all, descending the steps now; now the boy could see him.

"Don't you want to ride now?" he whispered. "We kin both ride now," the light within the house altering now, flaring up and sinking. *He's coming down the stairs now,* he thought. He had already ridden the mule up beside the horse block; presently his father was up behind him and he doubled the reins over and slashed the mule across the neck, but before the animal could begin to trot the hard, thin arm came round him, the hard, knotted hand jerking the mule back to a walk.

In the first red rays of the sun they were in the lot, putting plow gear on the mules. This time the sorrel mare was in the lot before he heard it at all, the rider collarless and even bareheaded, trembling, speaking in a shaking voice as the woman in the house had done, his father merely looking up once before stooping again to the hame he was buckling, so that the man on the mare spoke to his stooping back:

"You must realize you have ruined that rug. Wasn't there anybody here, any of your women . . ." he ceased, shaking, the boy watching him, the older brother leaning now in the stable door, chewing, blinking slowly and steadily at nothing apparently. "It cost a hundred dollars. But you never had a hundred dollars. You never will. So I'm going to charge you twenty bushels of corn against your crop. I'll add it in your contract and when you come to the commissary you can sign it. That won't keep Mrs. de Spain quiet but maybe it will teach you to wipe your feet off before you enter her house again."

Then he was gone. The boy looked at his father, who still had not spoken or even looked up again, who was now adjusting the loggerhead in the hame.

"Pap," he said. His father looked at him—the inscrutable face, the shaggy brows beneath which the gray eyes glinted coldly. Suddenly the boy went toward him, fast, stopping as suddenly. "You done the best you could!" he cried. "If he wanted hit done different why didn't he wait and tell you how? He won't git no twenty bushels! He won't git none! We'll gether hit and hide hit! I kin watch . . ."

"Did you put the cutter back in that straight stock like I told you?"

"No, sir," he said.

"Then go do it."

That was Wednesday. During the rest of that week he worked steadily, at what was within his scope and some which was beyond it, with an industry that did not need to be driven nor even commanded twice; he had this from his mother, with the difference that some at least of what he did he liked to do, such as splitting wood with the half-size axe which his mother and aunt had earned, or saved money somehow, to present him with at Christmas. In company with the two older women (and on one afternoon, even one of the sisters), he built pens for the shoat and the cow which were a part of his father's contract with the landlord, and one afternoon, his father being absent, gone somewhere on one of the mules, he went to the field.

They were running a middle buster now, his brother holding the plow straight while he handled the reins, and walking beside the straining mule, the rich black soil shearing cool and damp against his bare ankles, he thought *Maybe this is the end of it. Maybe even that twenty bushels that seems hard to have to pay for just a rug will be a cheap price for him to stop forever and always from being what he used to be;* thinking, dreaming now, so that his brother had to speak sharply to him to mind the mule: *Maybe he even won't collect the twenty bushels. Maybe it will all add up and balance and vanish—corn, rug, fire; the terror and grief, the being pulled two ways like between two teams of horses—gone, done with for ever and ever.*

Then it was Saturday; he looked up from beneath the mule he was harnessing and saw his father in the black coat and hat. "Not that," his father said. "The wagon gear." And then, two hours later, sitting in the wagon bed behind his father and brother on the seat, the wagon accomplished a final curve, and he saw the weathered paintless store with its tattered tobacco and patent-medicine posters and the tethered wagons and saddle animals below the gallery. He mounted the gnawed steps behind his father and brother, and there again was the lane of quiet, watching faces for the three of them to walk through. He saw the man in spectacles sitting at the plank table and he did not need to be told this was a Justice of the Peace; he sent one glare of fierce, exultant, partisan defiance at the man in collar and cravat now, whom he had seen but twice before in his life, and that on a galloping horse, who now wore on his face an expression not of rage but of amazed unbelief which the boy could not have known was at the incredible circumstance of being sued by one of his own tenants, and came and stood against his father and cried at the Justice: "He ain't done it! He ain't burnt . . ."

"Go back to the wagon," his father said.

"Burnt?" the Justice said. "Do I understand this rug was burned too?"

"Does anybody here claim it was?" his father said. "Go back to the wagon." But he did not, he merely retreated to the rear of the room, crowded as that other had been, but not to sit down this time, instead, to stand pressing among the motionless bodies, listening to the voices:

"And you claim twenty bushels of corn is too high for the damage you did to the rug?"

"He brought the rug to me and said he wanted the tracks washed out of it. I washed the tracks out and took the rug back to him."

"But you didn't carry the rug back to him in the same condition it was in before you made the tracks on it."

His father did not answer, and now for perhaps half a minute there was no sound at all save that of breathing, the faint, steady suspiration of complete and intent listening.

"You decline to answer that, Mr. Snopes?" Again his father did not answer. "I'm going to find against you, Mr. Snopes. I'm going to find that you were responsible for the injury to Major de Spain's rug and hold you liable for it. But twenty bushels of corn seems a little high for a man in your circumstances to have to pay. Major de Spain claims it cost a hundred dollars. October corn will be worth about fifty cents. I figure that if Major de Spain can stand a ninety-five dollar loss on something he paid cash for, you can stand a five-dollar loss you haven't earned yet. I hold you in damages to Major de Spain to the amount of ten bushels of corn over and above your contract with him, to be paid to him out of your crop at gathering time. Court adjourned."

It had taken no time hardly, the morning was but half begun. He thought they would return home and perhaps back to the field, since they were late, far behind all other farmers. But instead his father passed on behind the wagon, merely indicating with his hand for the older brother to follow with it, and he crossed the road toward the blacksmith shop opposite, pressing on after his father, overtaking him, speaking, whispering up at the harsh, calm face beneath the weathered hat: "He won't git no ten bushels neither. He won't git one. We'll . . ." until his father glanced for an instant down at him, the face absolutely calm, the grizzled eyebrows tangled above the cold eyes, the voice almost pleasant, almost gentle:

"You think so? Well, we'll wait till October anyway."

The matter of the wagon—the setting of a spoke or two and the tightening of the tires—did not take long either, the business of the tires accomplished by driving the wagon into the spring branch behind the shop and letting it stand there, the mules nuzzling into the water from time to time, and the boy on the seat with the idle reins, looking up the slope and through the sooty tunnel of the shed where the slow hammer rang and where his father sat on an upended cypress bolt, easily, either talking or listening, still sitting there when the boy brought the dripping wagon up out of the branch and halted it before the door.

"Take them on to the shade and hitch," his father said. He did so and returned. His father and the smith and a third man squatting on his heels inside the door were talking, about crops and animals; the boy, squatting too in the ammoniac dust and hoof parings and scales of rust, heard his father tell a long and unhurried story out of the time before the birth of the older brother even when he had been a professional horsetrader. And then his father came up beside him where he stood before a tattered last year's circus poster on the other side of the store, gazing rapt and quiet at the scarlet horses, the incredible poisings and convolutions of tulle and tights and the painted leers of comedians, and said, "It's time to eat."

But not at home. Squatting beside his brother against the front wall, he watched his father emerge from the store and produce from a paper sack a segment of cheese and divide it carefully and deliberately into three with his pocketknife and produce crackers from the same sack. They all three squatted on the gallery and ate, slowly, without talking; then in the store again, they drank from a tin dipper tepid water smelling of the cedar bucket and of living beech trees. And still they did not go home. It was a horse lot this time, a tall rail fence upon and along which men stood and sat and out of which one by one horses were led, to be walked and trotted and then cantered back and forth along the road while the slow swapping and buying went on and the sun began to slant westward, they—the three of them—watching and listening, the older brother with his muddy eyes and his steady, inevitable tobacco, the father commenting now and then on certain of the animals, to no one in particular.

It was after sundown when they reached home. They ate supper by lamplight, then, sitting on the doorstep, the boy watched the night fully accomplish, listening to the whippoorwills and the frogs, when he heard his mother's voice: "Abner! No! No! Oh, God. Oh, God. Abner!" and he rose, whirled, and saw the altered light through the door where a candle stub now burned in a bottle neck on the table and his father, still in the hat and coat, at once formal and burlesque as though dressed carefully for some shabby and ceremonial violence, emptying the reservoir of the lamp back into the five-gallon kerosene can from which it had been filled, while the mother tugged at his arm until he shifted the lamp to the other hand and flung her back, not savagely or viciously, just hard, into the wall, her hands flung out against the wall for balance, her mouth open and in her face the same quality of hopeless despair as had been in her voice. Then his father saw him standing in the door.

"Go to the barn and get that can of oil we were oiling the wagon with," he said. The boy did not move. Then he could speak.

"What . . ." he cried. "What are you . . ."

"Go get that oil," his father said. "Go."

Then he was moving, running, outside the house, toward the stable: this the old habit, the old blood which he had not been permitted to choose for himself, which had been bequeathed him willy-nilly and which had run for so long (and who knew where, battening on what of outrage and savagery and lust) before it came to him. *I could keep on,* he thought. *I could run on and on and never look back, never need to see his face again. Only I can't. I can't,* the rusted can in his hand now, the liquid sploshing in it as he ran back to the house and into it, into the sound of his mother's weeping in the next room, and handed the can to his father.

"Ain't you going to even send a nigger?" he cried. "At least you sent a nigger before!"

This time his father didn't strike him. The hand came even faster than the blow had, the same hand which had set the can on the table with almost excruciating care flashing from the can toward him too quick for him to follow it, gripping him by the back of the shirt and on to tiptoe before he had seen it quit the can, the face stooping at him in breathless and frozen ferocity, the cold, dead voice speaking over him to the older brother who leaned against the table, chewing with that steady, curious, sidewise motion of cows:

"Empty the can into the big one and go on. I'll catch up with you."

"Better tie him up to the bedpost," the brother said.

"Do like I told you," the father said. Then the boy was moving, his bunched shirt and the hard, bony hand between his shoulder blades, his toes just touching the floor, across the room and into the other one, past the sisters sitting with spread heavy thighs in the two chairs over the cold hearth, and to where his mother and aunt sat side by side on the bed, the aunt's arms about his mother's shoulders.

"Hold him," the father said. The aunt made a startled movement. "Not you," the father said. "Lennie. Take hold of him. I want to see you do it." His mother took him by the wrist. "You'll hold him better than that. If he gets loose don't you know what he is going to do? He will go up yonder." He jerked his head toward the road. "Maybe I'd better tie him."

"I'll hold him," his mother whispered.

"See you do then." Then his father was gone, the stiff foot heavy and measured upon the boards, ceasing at last.

Then he began to struggle. His mother caught him in both arms, he jerking and wrenching at them. He would be stronger in the end, he knew that. But he had no time to wait for it. "Lemme go!" he cried. "I don't want to have to hit you!"

"Let him go!" the aunt said. "If he don't go, before God, I am going up there myself!"

"Don't you see I can't?" his mother cried. "Sarty! Sarty! No! No! Help me, Lizzie!"

Then he was free. His aunt grasped at him but was too late. He whirled, running, his mother stumbled forward on to her knees behind him, crying to the nearer sister: "Catch him, Net! Catch him!" But that was too late too, the sister (the sisters were twins, born at the same time, yet either of them now gave the impression of being, encompassing as much living meat and volume and weight as any other two of the family) not yet having begun to rise from the chair, her head, face, alone merely turned, presenting to him in the flying instant an astonishing expanse of young female features untroubled by any surprise even, wearing only an expression of bovine interest. Then he was out of the room, out of the house, in the mild dust of the starlit road and the heavy rifeness of honeysuckle, the pale ribbon unspooling with terrific slowness under his running feet, reaching the gate at last and turning in, running, his heart and lungs drumming, on up the drive toward the lighted house, the lighted door. He did not knock, he burst in, sobbing for breath, incapable for the moment of speech; he saw the astonished face of the Negro in the linen jacket without knowing when the Negro had appeared.

"De Spain!" he cried, panted. "Where's . . . " then he saw the white man too emerging from a white door down the hall. "Barn!" he cried. "Barn!"

"What?" the white man said. "Barn?"

"Yes!" the boy cried. "Barn!"

"Catch him!" the white man shouted.

But it was too late this time too. The Negro grasped his shirt, but the entire sleeve, rotten with washing, carried away, and he was out that door too and in the drive again, and had actually never ceased to run even while he was screaming into the white man's face.

Behind him the white man was shouting, "My horse! Fetch my horse!" and he thought for an instant of cutting across the park and climbing the fence into the road, but he did not know the park nor how high the vine-massed fence might be and he dared not risk it. So he ran on down the drive, blood and breath roaring; presently he was in the road again though he could not see it. He could not hear either: the galloping mare was almost upon him before he heard her, and even then he held his course, as if the very urgency of his wild grief and need must in a

moment more find him wings, waiting until the ultimate instant
to hurl himself aside and into the weed-choked roadside ditch as
the horse thundered past and on, for an instant in furious silhouette against the stars, the tranquil early summer night sky
which, even before the shape of the horse and rider vanished,
strained abruptly and violently upward: a long, swirling roar
incredible and soundless, blotting the stars, and he springing up
and into the road again, running again, knowing it was too late
yet still running even after he heard the shot and, an instant
later, two shots, pausing now without knowing he had ceased to
run, crying "Pap! Pap!", running again before he knew he had
begun to run, stumbling, tripping over something and scrabbling up again without ceasing to run, looking backward over
his shoulder at the glare as he got up, running on among the
invisible trees, panting, sobbing, "Father! Father!"

At midnight he was sitting on the crest of a hill. He did not
know it was midnight and he did not know how far he had
come. But there was no glare behind him now and he sat now,
his back toward what he had called home for four days anyhow,
his face toward the dark woods which he would enter when
breath was strong again, small, shaking steadily in the chill
darkness, hugging himself into the remainder of his thin, rotten
shirt, the grief and despair now no longer terror and fear but
just grief and despair. *Father. My father,* he thought. "He was
brave!" he cried suddenly, aloud but not loud, no more than a
whisper: "He was! He was in the war! He was in Colonel
Sartoris' cav'ry!" not knowing that his father had gone to that
war a private in the fine old European sense, wearing no uniform, admitting the authority of and giving fidelity to no man
or army or flag, going to war as Malbrouck himself did: for
booty—it meant nothing and less than nothing to him if it were
enemy booty or his own.

The slow constellations wheeled on. It would be dawn and
then sun-up after a while and he would be hungry. But that
would be tomorrow and now he was only cold, and walking
would cure that. His breathing was easier now and he decided

to get up and go on, and then he found that he had been asleep because he knew it was almost dawn, the night almost over. He could tell that from the whippoorwills. They were everywhere now among the dark trees below him, constant and inflectioned and ceaseless, so that, as the instant for giving over to the day birds drew nearer and nearer, there was no interval at all between them. He got up. He was a little stiff, but walking would cure that too as it would the cold, and soon there would be the sun. He went on down the hill, toward the dark woods within which the liquid silver voices of the birds called unceasing—the rapid and urgent beating of the urgent and quiring heart of the late spring night. He did not look back. ᔑ

INTERPRETIVE QUESTIONS
FOR DISCUSSION

Why does Snopes soil and ruin the de Spains' rug?

1. Why does Snopes take Sarty with him when he goes to meet Major de Spain?

2. Why does Snopes feel such "ravening and jealous rage" toward the de Spains? (190)

3. Why does Snopes tell Sarty that it was "nigger sweat" that made the de Spains' house so "pretty and white"? Why does he add, "Maybe it ain't white enough yet to suit him. Maybe he wants to mix some white sweat with it"? (191)

4. Why does the author have Major de Spain make matters worse by demanding that Snopes clean the rug?

5. Why does Snopes go through the pretense of obeying Major de Spain's charge to clean the rug?

6. Why does Snopes return the rug when the de Spain household is sleeping?

7. Why does Snopes sue Major de Spain over the twenty bushels of corn before burning his barn?

8. Why is Snopes unable to accept the compromise settlement of owing Major de Spain an extra ten bushels of corn?

Suggested textual analyses
Pages 189–191: beginning, "I reckon I'll have a word with the man,"
and ending, "Maybe he wants to mix some white sweat with it."

Pages 195–196: beginning, " 'Pap,' he said. His father looked at him—"
and ending, *"done with for ever and ever."*

Why does Snopes burn the barns of the men he works for?

1. What kind of integrity is Snopes trying to preserve through fire? Why does fire speak "to some deep mainspring of his . . . being"? (187)

2. Why does Snopes refuse to fence his hog even though Mr. Harris, his employer, gives him the wire to do so?

3. Why doesn't Snopes show any appreciation or approval when Sarty fights the boy who hissed the words "barn burner"? (185)

4. Why are we told that Snopes's "wolflike independence" and "courage" impress strangers? Do they think they can benefit from him? (187)

5. Why does Snopes try to bring Sarty up to have respect for nobody, and to just "stick to your own blood"? (188)

6. Why is there no "heat or anger" in Snopes's cruelty? Why are all his actions performed without emotion? (188)

7. Why are we told that Snopes had previously been a professional horsetrader, and that he had gone to war strictly to acquire booty? (187, 198, 202)

8. Why doesn't Snopes wait until October, when his payment falls due to Major de Spain, to burn his barn?

Suggested textual analysis
Pages 186–188: beginning, "Get back in the wagon," and ending,
"Get on to bed. We'll be there tomorrow."

Why does Sarty break from his father and warn Major de Spain?

1. Why isn't Sarty able to say, "even to himself," that his father is a barn burner? Why, after the Harris barn burns, does Sarty imagine that his father might now be satisfied and not burn any more barns? (186)

2. When he thinks of his father, why does Sarty feel more "despair and grief" than "terror and fear"? (183, 184, 202)

3. Why does Sarty admit to his father that he would have told the Justice of the Peace that Snopes had burned Mr. Harris's barn?

4. Why does Sarty imagine that the "peace and dignity" of the de Spain residence will place it beyond his father's touch? Why does this thought fill him with "peace and joy"? (189)

5. Why does Sarty feel that he "can't" resist his father when he is ordered to get the oil for the barn burning? (199)

6. Why is Sarty filled with "wild grief and need" after he warns Major de Spain? Why does he run to warn his father also? (201)

7. Why does the author have Sarty's efforts to save the de Spains' barn fail?

8. At the end of the story, why does Sarty tell himself that his father was brave and fought in the war?

9. Why does the ten-year-old Sarty leave his home and family without looking back?

Suggested textual analyses

Pages 199–200: beginning, "Go to the barn and get that can of oil," and ending, "No! No! Help me, Lizzie!"

Pages 201–203: from "Behind him the white man was shouting," to the end of the story.

FOR FURTHER REFLECTION

1. Do you think Snopes is a purely evil person, or could he have amounted to something in a less class-conscious society?

2. Do all children have a natural morality akin to Sarty's, or is the capacity to determine right and wrong both developed and corrupted only through socialization?

3. Do you have any sympathy with the part of Snopes's integrity that refuses to be subjected by social superiors such as Major de Spain?

4. Can you rely on the law to protect you from the Snopeses of the world, or must you be ready to take things into your own hands?

5. Why are some people able to overcome the negative influences of their early childhood?

New African

Andrea Lee

ANDREA LEE (1953–   ) was born in Philadelphia and educated at Harvard University. Her first book, *Russian Journal,* a work of nonfiction, was nominated for a National Book Award and received the 1984 Jean Stein Award from the American Academy and Institute of Arts and Letters. Her first novel, *Sarah Phillips,* which Lee calls "a novel in stories," is based on her childhood as the daughter of a prominent African American Baptist minister and civil rights activist. In writing "New African," the central story in *Sarah Phillips,* Lee attempted to convey a different kind of truth, what she calls "truth of atmosphere—in rearranging and embellishing memories, [and] sharpening their significance by adding imaginary material. . . . I had license to trim, to twist, to steal from other lives, to invent."

ON A HOT Sunday morning in the summer of 1963, I was sitting restlessly with my mother, my brother Matthew, and my aunts Lily, Emma, and May in a central pew of the New African Baptist Church. It was mid-August, and the hum of the big electric fans at the back of the church was almost enough to muffle my father's voice from the pulpit; behind me I could hear Mrs. Gordon, a stout, feeble old woman who always complained of dizziness, remark sharply to her daughter that at the rate the air-conditioning fund was growing, it might as well be for the next century. Facing the congregation, my father—who was Reverend Phillips to the rest of the world—seemed hot himself; he mopped his brow with a handkerchief and drank several glasses of ice water from the heavy pitcher on the table by the pulpit. I looked at him critically. He's still reading the text, I thought. Then he'll do the sermon, then the baptism, and it will be an hour, maybe two.

I rubbed my chin and then idly began to snap the elastic band that held my red straw hat in place. What I would really like to do, I decided, would be to go home, put on my shorts, and climb up into the tree house I had set up the day before with Matthew. We'd nailed an old bushelbasket up in the branches of the big maple that stretched above the sidewalk in front of the house; it made a sort of crow's nest where you could sit comfortably, except for a few splinters, and read, or peer through the dusty leaves at the cars that passed down the quiet suburban road. There was shade and wind and a feeling of high adventure up in the treetop, where the air seemed to vibrate with the dry rhythms of the cicadas; it was as different as possible from church, where the packed congregation sat in a near-visible miasma of emotion and cologne, and trolleys passing in the city street outside set the stained-glass windows rattling.

I slouched between Mama and Aunt Lily and felt myself going limp with lassitude and boredom, as if the heat had melted my bones; the only thing about me with any character seemed to be my firmly starched eyelet dress. Below the scalloped hem, my legs were skinny and wiry, the legs of a ten-year-old amazon, scarred from violent adventures with bicycles and skates. A fingernail tapped my wrist; it was Aunt Emma, reaching across Aunt Lily to press a piece of butterscotch into my hand. When I slipped the candy into my mouth, it tasted faintly of Arpège; my mother and her three sisters were monumental women, ample of bust and slim of ankle, with a weakness for elegant footwear and French perfume. As they leaned back and forth to exchange discreet tidbits of gossip, they fanned themselves and me with fans from the Byron J. Wiggins Funeral Parlor. The fans, which were fluttering throughout the church, bore a depiction of the Good Shepherd: a hollow-eyed blond Christ holding three fat pink-cheeked children. This Christ resembled the Christ who stood among apostles on the stained-glass windows of the church. Deacon Wiggins, a thoughtful man, had also provided New African with a few dozen fans bearing the picture of a black child praying, but I rarely saw those in use.

There was little that was new or very African about the New
African Baptist Church. The original congregation had been
formed in 1813 by three young men from Philadelphia's large
community of free blacks, and before many generations had
passed, it had become spiritual home to a collection of prosper-
ous, conservative, generally light-skinned parishioners. The
church was a gray Gothic structure, set on the corner of a run-
down street in South Philadelphia a dozen blocks below
Rittenhouse Square and a few blocks west of the spare, clannish
Italian neighborhoods that produced Frankie Avalon and Frank
Rizzo. At the turn of the century, the neighborhood had been a
tidy collection of brick houses with scrubbed marble steps—the
homes of a group of solid citizens whom Booker T. Washington,
in a centennial address to the church, described as "the ablest
Negro businessmen of our generation." Here my father had
grown up aspiring to preach to the congregation of New
African—an ambition encouraged by my grandmother Phillips,
a formidable churchwoman. Here, too, my mother and her sisters had walked with linked arms to Sunday services,
exchanging affected little catchphrases of French and Latin they
had learned at Girls' High.

In the 1950s many of the parishioners, seized by the national
urge toward the suburbs, moved to newly integrated towns outside the city, leaving the streets around New African to fill with
bottles and papers and loungers. The big church stood suddenly
isolated. It had not been abandoned—on Sundays the front steps
overflowed with members who had driven in—but there was
a tentative feeling in the atmosphere of those Sunday mornings,
as if through the muddle of social change, the future of
New African had become unclear. Matthew and I, suburban
children, felt a mixture of pride and animosity toward the
church. On the one hand, it was a marvelous private domain, a
richly decorated and infinitely suggestive playground where we
were petted by a congregation that adored our father; on the
other hand, it seemed a bit like a dreadful old relative in the city,

one who forced us into tedious visits and who linked us to a past that came to seem embarrassingly primitive as we grew older.

I slid down in my seat, let my head roll back, and looked up at the blue arches of the church ceiling. Lower than these, in back of the altar, was an enormous gilded cross. Still lower, in a semi-circle near the pulpit, sat the choir, flanked by two tall golden files of organ pipes, and below the choir was a somber crescent of dark-suited deacons. In front, at the center of everything, his bald head gleaming under the lights, was Daddy. On summer Sundays he wore white robes, and when he raised his arms, the heavy material fell in curving folds like the ridged petals of an Easter lily. Usually when I came through the crowd to kiss him after the service, his cheek against my lips felt wet and gravelly with sweat and a new growth of beard sprouted since morning. Today, however, was a baptismal Sunday, and I wouldn't have a chance to kiss him until he was freshly shaven and cool from the shower he took after the ceremony. The baptismal pool was in an alcove to the left of the altar; it had mirrored walls and red velvet curtains, and above it, swaying on a string, hung a stuffed white dove.

Daddy paused in the invocation and asked the congregation to pray. The choir began to sing softly:

Blessed assurance,
Jesus is mine!
Oh what a foretaste
Of glory divine!

In the middle of the hymn, I edged my head around my mother's cool, muscular arm (she swam every day of the summer) and peered at Matthew. He was sitting bolt upright holding a hymnal and a pencil, his long legs inside his navy-blue summer suit planted neatly in front of him, his freckled thirteen-year-old face that was so like my father's wearing not the demonic grin it bore when we played alone but a maddeningly composed, attentive expression. "Two hours!" I mouthed at him, and pulled back at a warning pressure from my mother. Then I joined in the singing, feeling disappointed: Matthew had returned me a glance of scorn. Just lately he had started acting very superior and tolerant about tedious Sunday mornings. A month before, he'd been baptized, marching up to the pool in a line of white-robed children as the congregation murmured happily about Reverend Phillips's son. Afterward Mrs. Pinkston, a tiny, yellow-skinned old woman with a blind left eye, had come up to me and given me a painful hug, whispering that she was praying night and day for the pastor's daughter to hear the call as well.

I bit my fingernails whenever I thought about baptism; the subject brought out a deep-rooted balkiness in me. Ever since I could remember, Matthew and I had made a game of dispelling the mysteries of worship with a gleeful secular eye: we knew how the bread and wine were prepared for Communion, and where Daddy bought his robes (Ekhardt Brothers, in North Philadelphia, makers also of robes for choirs, academicians, and judges). Yet there was an unassailable magic about an act as public and dramatic as baptism. I felt toward it the slightly exasperated awe a stagehand might feel on realizing that although he can identify with professional exactitude the minutest components of a show, there is still something indefinable in the power that makes it a cohesive whole. Though I could not have put it into words, I believed that the decision to make a frightening and embarrassing backward plunge into a pool of sanctified water meant that one had received a summons to Christianity as unmistakable as the blare of an automobile horn. I believed this with the same fervor with which, already, I believed in the power of romance, especially in the miraculous efficacy of a lover's first kiss. I had never been kissed by a lover, nor had I heard the call to baptism.

For a Baptist minister and his wife, my father and mother were unusually relaxed about religion; Matthew and I had never been required to read the Bible, and my father's sermons had been criticized by some older church members for omitting the word "sin." Mama and Daddy never tried to push me toward baptism, but a number of other people did. Often on holidays, when I had retreated from the noise of the family dinner table and sat trying to read in my favorite place (the window seat in Matthew's room, with the curtains drawn to form a tent), Aunt Lily would come and find me. Aunt Lily was the youngest of my mother's sisters, a kindergarten teacher with the fatally over-developed air of quaintness that is the infallible mark of an old maid. Aunt Lily hoped and hoped again with various suitors, but even I knew she would never find a husband. I respected her because she gave me wonderful books of fairy tales, inscribed in her neat, loopy hand; when she talked about religion, however, she assumed an anxious, flirtatious air that made me cringe. "Well, Miss Sarah, what are you scared of?" she would ask, tug-ging gently on one of my braids and bringing her plump face so close to mine that I could see her powder, which was, in accor-dance with the custom of fashionable colored ladies, several shades lighter than her olive skin. "God isn't anyone to be afraid of!" she'd continue as I looked at her with my best deadpan expression. "He's someone nice, just as nice as your daddy"—I had always suspected Aunt Lily of having a crush on my father—"and he loves you, in the same way your daddy does!"

"You would make us all so happy!" I was told at different times by Aunt Lily, Aunt Emma, and Aunt May. The only peo-ple who said nothing at all were Mama and Daddy, but I sensed in them a thoughtful, suppressed wistfulness that maddened me.

After the hymn, Daddy read aloud a few verses from the third chapter of Luke, verses I recognized in the almost instinctive way in which I was familiar with all of the well-traveled parts of the Old and New Testaments. "Prepare the way of the Lord, make his paths straight," read my father in a mild voice. "Every valley shall be filled, and every mountain and hill shall be brought low, and the crooked shall be made straight, and the rough paths made smooth, and all flesh shall see the salvation of God."

He had a habit of pausing to fix his gaze on part of the con-gregation as he read, and that Sunday he seemed to be talking to a small group of strangers who sat in the front row. These visitors were young white men and women, students from Philadelphia colleges, who for the past year had been coming to hear him talk. It was hard to tell them apart: all the men seemed to have beards, and the women wore their hair long and straight. Their informal clothes stood out in that elaborate assembly, and church members whispered angrily that the young women didn't wear hats. I found the students appealing and rather romantic, with their earnest eyes and timid air of being perpetually sorry about something. It was clear that they had good intentions, and I couldn't understand why so many of the adults in the congregation seemed to dislike them so much. After services, they would hover around Daddy. "Never a more beautiful civil rights sermon!" they would say in low, fervent voices. Sometimes they seemed to have tears in their eyes.

I wasn't impressed by their praise of my father; it was only what everyone said. People called him a champion of civil rights; he gave speeches on the radio, and occasionally he appeared on television. (The first time I'd seen him on Channel 5, I'd been gravely disappointed by the way he looked: the bright lights exaggerated the furrows that ran between his nose and mouth, and his narrow eyes gave him a sinister air; he looked like an Oriental villain in a Saturday afternoon thriller.) During the past year he had organized a boycott that integrated the staff of a huge frozen-food plant in Philadelphia, and he'd been away several times to attend marches and meetings in the South. I was privately embarrassed to have a parent who freely admitted going to jail in Alabama, but the students who visited New African seemed to think it almost miraculous. Their conversations with my father were peppered with references to places I had never seen, towns I imagined as being swathed in a mist of darkness visible: Selma, Macon, Birmingham, Biloxi.

Matthew and I had long ago observed that what Daddy generally did in his sermons was to speak very softly and then surprise everyone with a shout. Of course, I knew that there was more to it than that; even in those days I recognized a genius of personality in my father. He loved crowds, handling them with the expert good humor of a man entirely in his element. At church banquets, at the vast annual picnic that was held beside a lake in New Jersey, or at any gathering in the backyards and living rooms of the town where we lived, the sound I heard most often was the booming of my father's voice followed by shouts of laughter from the people around him. He had a passion for oratory; at home, he infuriated Matthew and me by staging absurd debates at the dinner table, verbal melees that he won quite selfishly, with a loud crow of delight at his own virtuosity. "Is a fruit a vegetable?" he would demand. "Is a zipper a machine?" Matthew and I would plead with him to be quiet as we strained to get our own points across, but it was no use. When the last word had resounded and we sat looking at him in irritated silence, he would clear his throat, settle his collar, and resume eating, his face still glowing with an irrepressible glee.

When he preached, he showed the same private delight. A look of rapt pleasure seemed to broaden and brighten the contours of his angular face until it actually appeared to give off light as he spoke. He could preach in two very different ways. One was the delicate, sonorous idiom of formal oratory, with which he must have won the prizes he held from his seminary days. The second was a hectoring, insinuating, incantatory tone, full of the rhythms of the South he had never lived in, linking him to generations of thunderous Baptist preachers. When he used this tone, as he was doing now, affectionate laughter rippled through the pews.

"I know," he said, looking out over the congregation and blinking his eyes rapidly, "that there are certain people in this room—oh, I don't have to name names or point a finger—who have ignored that small true voice, the voice that is the voice of Jesus calling out in the shadowy depths of the soul. And while you all are looking around and wondering just who those 'certain people' are, I want to tell you all a secret: they are you and me, and your brother-in-law, and every man, woman, and child in this room this morning. All of us listen to our bellies when they tell us it is time to eat, we pay attention to our eyes when they grow heavy from wanting sleep, but when it comes to the sacred knowledge our hearts can offer, we are deaf, dumb, blind, and senseless. Throw away that blindness, that deafness, that sulky indifference. When all the world lies to you, Jesus will tell you what is right. Listen to him. Call on him. In these times of confusion, when there are a dozen different ways to turn, and Mama and Papa can't help you, trust Jesus to set you straight. Listen to him. The Son of God has the answers. Call on him. Call on him. Call on him."

The sermon was punctuated with an occasional loud "Amen!" from Miss Middleton, an excitable old lady whose eyes flashed defiantly at the reproving faces of those around her. New African was not the kind of Baptist church where shouting was a normal part of the service; I occasionally heard my father mock the staid congregation by calling it Saint African. Whenever Miss Middleton loosed her tongue (sometimes she went off into fits of rapturous shrieks and had to be helped out of the service by the church nurse), my mother and aunts exchanged grimaces and shrugged, as if confronted by incomprehensibly barbarous behavior.

When Daddy had spoken the final words of the sermon, he drank a glass of water and vanished through a set of red velvet curtains to the right of the altar. At the same time, the choir began to sing what was described in the church bulletin as a "selection." These selections were always arenas for the running dispute between the choirmaster and the choir. Jordan Grimes, the choirmaster, was a Curtis graduate who was partial to Handel, but the choir preferred artistic spirituals performed in the lush, heroic style of Paul Robeson. Grimes had triumphed that Sunday. As the choir gave a spirited but unwilling rendition of Agnus Dei, I watched old Deacon West smile in approval. A Spanish-American War veteran, he admitted to being ninety-four but was said to be older; his round yellowish face, otherwise unwrinkled, bore three deep, deliberate-looking horizontal creases on the brow, like carvings on a scarab. "That old man is as flirtatious as a boy of twenty!" my mother often said, watching his stiff, courtly movements among the ladies of the church. Sometimes he gave me a dry kiss and a piece of peppermint candy after the service; I liked his crackling white collars and smell of bay rum.

The selection ended; Jordan Grimes struck two deep chords on the organ, and the lights in the church went low. A subtle stir ran through the congregation, and I moved closer to my mother. This was the moment that fascinated and disturbed me more than anything else at church: the prelude to the ceremony of baptism. Deacon West rose and drew open the draperies that had been closed around the baptismal pool, and there stood my father in water to his waist. The choir began to sing:

We're marching to Zion,
Beautiful, beautiful Zion,
We're marching upward to Zion,
The beautiful city of God!

Down the aisle, guided by two church mothers, came a procession of eight children and adolescents. They wore white robes, the girls with white ribbons in their hair, and they all had solemn expressions of terror on their faces. I knew each one of them. There was Billy Price, a big, slow-moving boy of thirteen, the son of Deacon Price. There were the Duckery twins. There was Caroline Piggee, whom I hated because of her long, soft black curls, her dimpled pink face, and her lisp that ravished grownups. There was Georgie Battis and Sue Anne Ivory, and Wendell and Mabel Cullen.

My mother gave me a nudge. "Run up to the side of the pool!" she whispered. It was the custom for unbaptized children to watch the ceremony from the front of the church. They sat on the knees of the deacons and church mothers, and it was not unusual for a child to volunteer then and there for next month's baptism. I made my way quickly down the dark aisle, feeling the carpet slip under the smooth soles of my patent-leather shoes.

When I reached the side of the pool, I sat down in the bony lap of Bessie Gray, an old woman who often took care of Matthew and me when our parents were away; we called her Aunt Bessie. She was a fanatically devout Christian whose strict ideas on child-rearing had evolved over decades of domestic service to a rich white family in Delaware. The link between us, a mixture of hostility and grudging affection, had been forged in hours of pitched battles over bedtimes and proper behavior. Her worshipful respect for my father, whom she called "the Rev," was exceeded only by her pride—the malice-tinged pride of an omniscient family servant—in her "white children," to whom she often unflatteringly compared Matthew and me. It was easy to see why my mother and her circle of fashionable matrons described Bessie Gray as "archaic"—one had only to look at her black straw hat attached with three enormous old-fashioned pins to her knot of frizzy white hair. Her lean, brown-skinned face was dominated by a hawk nose inherited from some Indian ancestor and punctuated by a big black mole; her eyes were small, shrewd, and baleful. She talked in ways that were already passing into history and parody, and she wore a thick orange face powder that smelled like dead leaves.

I leaned against her spare bosom and watched the other children clustered near the pool, their bonnets and hair ribbons and round heads outlined in the dim light. For a minute it was very still. Somewhere in the hot, darkened church a baby gave a fretful murmur; from outside came the sound of cars passing in the street. The candidates for baptism, looking stiff and self-conscious, stood lined up on the short stairway leading to the pool. Sue Anne Ivory fiddled with her sleeve and then put her fingers in her mouth.

Daddy spoke the opening phrases of the ceremony: "In the Baptist Church, we do not baptize infants, but believe that a person must choose salvation for himself."

I didn't listen to the words; what I noticed was the music of the whole—how the big voice darkened and lightened in tone,

and how the grand architecture of the Biblical sentences enno-
bled the voice. The story, of course, was about Jesus and John
the Baptist. One phrase struck me newly each time: "This is my
beloved son, in whom I am well pleased!" Daddy sang out these
words in a clear, triumphant tone, and the choir echoed him.
Ever since I could understand it, this phrase had made me feel
melancholy; it seemed to expose a hard knot of disobedience
that had always lain inside me. When I heard it, I thought envi-
ously of Matthew, for whom life seemed to be a sedate and
ordered affair: he, not I, was a child in whom a father could be
well pleased.

Daddy beckoned to Billy Price, the first baptismal candidate
in line, and Billy, ungainly in his white robe, descended the steps
into the pool. In soft, slow voices the choir began to sing:

Wade in the water,
Wade in the water, children,
Wade in the water,
God gonna trouble
The water.

In spite of Jordan Grimes's efforts, the choir swayed like a
gospel chorus as it sang this spiritual; the result was to add an
eerie jazz beat to the minor chords. The music gave me goose-
flesh. Daddy had told me that this was the same song that the
slaves had sung long ago in the South, when they gathered to be
baptized in rivers and streams. Although I cared little about history, and found it hard to picture the slaves as being any
ancestors of mine, I could clearly imagine them coming together
beside a broad muddy river that wound away between trees
drooping with strange vegetation. They walked silently in lines,
their faces very black against their white clothes, leading their
children. The whole scene was bathed in the heavy golden light
that meant age and solemnity, the same light that seemed to
weigh down the Israelites in illustrated volumes of Bible stories,
and that shone now from the baptismal pool, giving the ceremony the air of a spectacle staged in a dream.

All attention in the darkened auditorium was now focused on the pool, where between the red curtains my father stood holding Billy Price by the shoulders. Daddy stared into Billy's face, and the boy stared back, his lips set and trembling. "And now, by the power invested in me," said Daddy, "I baptize you in the name of the Father, the Son, and the Holy Ghost." As he pronounced these words, he conveyed a tenderness as efficient and impersonal as a physician's professional manner; beneath it, however, I could see a strong private gladness, the same delight that transformed his face when he preached a sermon. He paused to flick a drop of water off his forehead, and then, with a single smooth, powerful motion of his arms, he laid Billy Price back into the water as if he were putting an infant to bed. I caught my breath as the boy went backward. When he came up, sputtering, two church mothers helped him out of the pool and through a doorway into a room where he would be dried and dressed. Daddy shook water from his hands and gave a slight smile as another child entered the pool.

One by one, the baptismal candidates descended the steps. Sue Anne Ivory began to cry and had to be comforted. Caroline Piggee blushed and looked up at my father with such a coquettish air that I jealously wondered how he could stand it. After a few baptisms my attention wandered, and I began to gnaw the edge of my thumb and to peer at the pale faces of the visiting college students. Then I thought about Matthew, who had punched me in the arm that morning and had shouted, "No punchbacks!" I thought as well about a collection of horse chestnuts I meant to assemble in the fall, and about two books, one whose subject was adults and divorces, and another, by E. Nesbit, that continued the adventures of the Bastable children.

After Wendell Cullen had left the water (glancing uneasily back at the wet robe trailing behind him), Daddy stood alone among the curtains and the mirrors. The moving reflections from the pool made the stuffed dove hanging over him seem to flutter on its string. "Dear Lord," said Daddy, as Jordan Grimes struck a chord, "bless these children who have chosen to be baptized in accordance with your teaching, and who have been reborn to carry out your work. In each of them, surely, you are well pleased." He paused, staring out into the darkened auditorium. "And if there is anyone out there—man, woman, child—who wishes to be baptized next month, let him come forward now." He glanced around eagerly. "Oh, do come forward and give Christ your heart and give me your hand!"

Just then Aunt Bessie gave me a little shake and whispered sharply, "Go on up and accept Jesus!"

I stiffened and dug my bitten fingernails into my palms. The last clash of wills I had had with Aunt Bessie had been when she, crazily set in her old Southern attitudes, had tried to make me wear an enormous straw hat, as her "white children" did, when I played outside in the sun. The old woman had driven me to madness, and I had ended up spanked and sullen, crouching moodily under the dining-room table. But this was different, outrageous, none of her business, I thought. I shook my head violently and she took advantage of the darkness in the church to seize both of my shoulders and jounce me with considerable roughness, whispering, "Now, listen, young lady! Your daddy up there is calling you to Christ. Your big brother has already offered his soul to the Lord. Now Daddy wants his little girl to step forward."

"No, he doesn't." I glanced at the baptismal pool, where my father was clasping the hand of a strange man who had come up to him. I hoped that this would distract Aunt Bessie, but she was tireless.

"Your mama and your aunt Lily and your aunt May all want you to answer the call. You're hurting them when you say no to Jesus."

"No, I'm not!" I spoke out loud and I saw the people nearby turn to look at me. At the sound of my voice, Daddy, who was a few yards away, faltered for a minute in what he was saying and glanced over in my direction.

Aunt Bessie seemed to lose her head. She stood up abruptly, pulling me with her, and, while I was still frozen in a dreadful paralysis, tried to drag me down the aisle toward my father. The two of us began a brief struggle that could not have lasted for more than a few seconds but that seemed an endless mortal conflict—my slippery patent-leather shoes braced against the floor, my straw hat sliding cockeyed and lodging against one ear, my right arm twisting and twisting in the iron circle of the old woman's grip, my nostrils full of the dead-leaf smell of her powder and black skirts. In an instant I had wrenched my arm free and darted up the aisle toward Mama, my aunts, and Matthew. As I slipped past the pews in the darkness, I imagined that I could feel eyes fixed on me and hear whispers. "What'd you do, dummy?" whispered Matthew, tugging on my sash as I reached our pew, but I pushed past him without answering. Although it was hot in the church, my teeth were chattering: it was the first time I had won a battle with a grownup, and the earth seemed to be about to cave in beneath me. I squeezed in between Mama and Aunt Lily just as the lights came back on in the church. In the baptismal pool, Daddy raised his arms for the last time. "The Lord bless you and keep you," came his big voice. "The Lord be gracious unto you, and give you peace."

What was curious was how uncannily subdued my parents were when they heard of my skirmish with Aunt Bessie. Normally they were swift to punish Matthew and me for misbehavior in church and for breaches in politeness toward adults; this episode combined the two, and smacked of sacrilege besides. Yet once I had made an unwilling apology to the old woman (as I kissed her she shot me such a vengeful glare that I realized that forever after it was to be war to the death between the two of us), I was permitted, once we had driven home, to climb up into the green shade of the big maple tree I had dreamed of throughout the service. In those days, more than now, I fell away into a remote dimension whenever I opened a book; that afternoon, as I sat with rings of sunlight and shadow moving over my arms and legs, and winged yellow seeds plopping down on the pages of *The Story of the Treasure Seekers*, I felt a vague uneasiness floating in the back of my mind—a sense of having misplaced something, of being myself misplaced. I was holding myself quite aloof from considering what had happened, as I did with most serious events, but through the adventures of the Bastables I kept remembering the way my father had looked when he'd heard what had happened. He hadn't looked severe or angry, but merely puzzled, and he had regarded me with the same puzzled expression, as if he'd just discovered that I existed and didn't know what to do with me. "What happened, Sairy?" he asked, using an old baby nickname, and I said, "I didn't want to go up there." I hadn't cried at all, and that was another curious thing.

After that Sunday, through some adjustment in the adult spheres beyond my perception, all pressure on me to accept baptism ceased. I turned twelve, fifteen, then eighteen without being baptized, a fact that scandalized some of the congregation; however, my parents, who openly discussed everything else, never said a word to me. The issue, and the episode that had illuminated it, was surrounded by a clear ring of silence that, for our garrulous family, was something close to supernatural. I continued to go to New African—in fact, continued after Matthew, who dropped out abruptly during his freshman year in college; the ambiguousness in my relations with the old church gave me at times an inflated sense of privilege (I saw myself as a romantically isolated religious heroine, a sort of self-made Baptist martyr) and at other times a feeling of loss that I was too proud ever to acknowledge. I never went up to take my father's hand, and he never commented upon that fact to me. It was an odd pact, one that I could never consider in the light of day; I stored it in the subchambers of my heart and mind. It was only much later, after he died, and I left New African forever, that I began to examine the peculiar gift of freedom my father—whose entire soul was in the church, and in his exuberant, bewitching tongue—had granted me through his silence. ◞

INTERPRETIVE QUESTIONS
FOR DISCUSSION

**Why does Sarah refuse to be baptized into the New African
Baptist Church?**

1. Why does the subject of baptism bring out "a deep-rooted
   balkiness" in Sarah? (215)

2. Why does Sarah compare the church to a "dreadful old relative
   in the city"? Why does Sarah call its past "embarrassingly
   primitive"? (213, 214)

3. Why does Sarah believe that the call to Christianity should be
   "as unmistakable as the blare of an automobile horn"?
   Why does she compare the power of baptism to the power
   of romance? (215)

4. Why is the prelude to the baptismal ceremony, when her father
   appears waist deep in the baptismal pool, the moment that
   disturbs Sarah the most?

5. Why does her father's reading of the Biblical phrase "This is my
   beloved son, in whom I am well pleased!" make Sarah compare
   herself unfavorably to Matthew? Why does the phrase have the
   effect of exposing a "hard knot of disobedience that had always
   lain inside" her? (222)

6. Why does Sarah refuse Aunt Bessie's command to "go on up and
   accept Jesus" by insisting that her Daddy *doesn't* want her to
   step forward? (224)

7. Why does her brief struggle with Aunt Bessie seem to Sarah "an endless mortal conflict"? Why does Sarah's victory—her first ever over a grownup—leave her with the feeling that the earth was about to cave in beneath her? (224–225)

8. Why does Sarah prefer the solitude and "high adventure" of her tree house to the "near-visible miasma of emotion" of her father's church? (212)

Suggested textual analyses

Page 215: beginning, "I bit my fingernails," and ending, "nor had I heard the call to baptism."

Page 224: beginning, "I stiffened and dug my bitten fingernails," and ending, "glanced over in my direction."

Why do Sarah's parents never mention her refusal to be baptized, when the rest of the congregation is "scandalized" by it?

1. Why do Sarah's parents insure that all adult pressure on her to accept baptism ceases after her battle with Aunt Bessie?

2. Why does Sarah's fight with Aunt Bessie make Sarah's father regard her as if he'd just discovered that she existed?

3. Why do so many members of the congregation put pressure on Sarah to become baptized, considering that in the Baptist Church it is believed "a person must choose salvation for himself"? (221)

4. Why does Sarah describe her father as having a "genius of personality"? (217–218)

5. Why are we told that Sarah's father had two styles of preaching: the "sonorous idiom of formal oratory" and an "incantatory tone, full of the rhythms of the South he had never lived in"? (218)

6. Why are the young white visitors at New African more impressed with Sarah's father's civil rights work than she is?

7. Why are Sarah and Matthew infuriated with their father for staging dinner-table debates that he wins "quite selfishly"? (218)

8. What does Sarah mean when she says that, through his silence, her father granted her a "peculiar gift of freedom"? (226)

Suggested textual analysis
Pages 217–218: beginning, "Matthew and I had long ago observed," and ending, "affectionate laughter rippled through the pews."

Why does Sarah continue going to New African, long after she refuses to be baptized?

1. Why does the public act of baptism have an "unassailable magic" for Sarah? (215)

2. Why do Sarah and Matthew feel both "pride and animosity" toward New African? (213)

3. Why does Sarah emphasize that little was new or African about the New African Baptist Church?

4. Why are we told that Sarah can't imagine having slaves for ancestors?

5. Why does Sarah experience an uneasy sense of being "misplaced" after her victory over Aunt Bessie? (226)

6. Why does Sarah hold herself "aloof" from considering what had happened as a result of her skirmish with Aunt Bessie? (226)

7. Why does refusing to be baptized make Sarah feel like a "romantically isolated religious heroine, a sort of self-made Baptist martyr"? (226)

8. What is the sense of loss with regard to New African that Sarah is "too proud" to acknowledge? (226)

Suggested textual analysis
Page 226: from "After that Sunday," to the end of the story.

FOR FURTHER REFLECTION

1. Why do children need the "gift of freedom"?

2. Should children be allowed to decide religious matters for themselves?

3. Is a liberal parent, like Sarah's father, or a punitive parent, like Snopes in "Barn Burning," more likely to have the greater influence in the formation of a child's character?

4. Did Sarah make the right choice in deciding not to be baptized?

5. How can we as parents raise our children to have a social conscience and work to better society, if not through our participation in religious communities like the New African Baptist Church?

6. Why is the pleasure of freedom—whether religious, political, or personal—almost always equivocal?

LETTER TO HIS FATHER

❦

THE JUDGMENT

Franz Kafka

FRANZ KAFKA (1883–1924) was born in
Prague of German-speaking Jewish parents.
After earning a doctorate in law, he began a
successful career as a state insurance lawyer.
By night he wrote novels and stories. For
years Kafka wished to marry, and tried to,
but could not convince himself to do it:
"All that I have accomplished is the result of
being alone," he said. "I consist of literature
and am unable to be anything else." In 1913
Kafka wrote to his publisher, asking him to
print three of his short works, "The Stoker,"
"The Metamorphosis," and Judgment," in
a single volume called *The Sons*. In addition
to the "obvious connection" between them,
there was, he claimed, a "secret one."
Kafka wrote the "Letter to His Father"
in 1919, where he makes explicit the secret
connection. Kafka showed the letter to
his mother, but never sent it to his father.
Kafka died of tuberculosis four and a
half years later—unmarried and still
"a son"—hoping that none of his work
would remain in print.

Letter to His Father

DEAREST FATHER,

You asked me recently why I maintain that I am afraid of you. As usual, I was unable to think of any answer to your question, partly for the very reason that I am afraid of you, and partly because an explanation of the grounds for this fear would mean going into far more details than I could even approximately keep in mind while talking. And if I now try to give you an answer in writing, it will still be very incomplete, because, even in writing, this fear and its consequences hamper me in relation to you and because the magnitude of the subject goes far beyond the scope of my memory and power of reasoning.

To you the matter always seemed very simple, at least insofar as you talked about it in front of me, and indiscriminately in front of many other people. It looked to you more or less as follows: you have worked hard all your life, have sacrificed everything for your children, above all for me, consequently I have lived high and handsome, have been completely at liberty to learn whatever I wanted, and have had no cause for material worries, which means worries of any kind at all. You have not expected any gratitude for this, knowing what "children's gratitude" is like, but have expected at least some sort of obligingness, some sign of sympathy. Instead I have always hidden from you, in my room, among my books, with crazy friends, or with crackpot ideas. I have never talked to you frankly; I have never come to you when you were in the synagogue, never visited you at Franzensbad, nor indeed ever shown any family feeling; I have never taken any interest in the business or your other concerns; I saddled you with the factory and walked off; I encouraged Ottla in her obstinacy, and never lifted a finger for you (never even got you a theater ticket), while I do everything for my friends. If you sum up your judgment of me, the result you get is that, although you don't charge me with anything downright improper or wicked (with the exception perhaps of my latest marriage plan), you do charge me with coldness, estrangement, and ingratitude. And, what is more, you charge me with it in such a way as to make it seem my fault, as though I might have been able, with something like a touch on the steering wheel, to make everything quite different, while you aren't in the slightest to blame, unless it be for having been too good to me.

This, your usual way of representing it, I regard as accurate only insofar as I too believe you are entirely blameless in the matter of our estrangement. But I am equally entirely blameless. If I could get you to acknowledge this, then what would be possible is not, I think, a new life—we are both much too old for that—but still, a kind of peace; no cessation, but still, a diminution of your unceasing reproaches.

Oddly enough you have some sort of notion of what I mean. For instance, a short time ago you said to me: "I have always been fond of you, even though outwardly I didn't act toward you as other fathers generally do, and this precisely because I can't pretend as other people can." Now, Father, on the whole I have never doubted your goodness toward me, but this remark

I consider wrong. You can't pretend, that is true, but merely for that reason to maintain that other fathers pretend is either mere opinionatedness, and as such beyond discussion, or on the other hand—and this in my view is what it really is—a veiled expression of the fact that something is wrong in our relationship and that you have played your part in causing it to be so, but without its being your fault. If you really mean that, then we are in agreement.

I'm not going to say, of course, that I have become what I am only as a result of your influence. That would be very much exaggerated (and I am indeed inclined to this exaggeration). It is indeed quite possible that even if I had grown up entirely free from your influence I still could not have become a person after your own heart. I should probably have still become a weakly, timid, hesitant, restless person, neither Robert Kafka nor Karl Hermann, but yet quite different from what I really am, and we might have got on with each other excellently. I should have been happy to have you as a friend, as a boss, an uncle, a grandfather, even (though rather more hesitantly) as a father-in-law. Only as a father you have been too strong for me, particularly since my brothers died when they were small and my sisters came along only much later, so that I alone had to bear the brunt of it—and for that I was much too weak.

Compare the two of us: I, to put it in a very much abbreviated form, a Löwy with a certain Kafka component, which, however, is not set in motion by the Kafka will to life, business, and conquest, but by a Löwyish spur that impels more secretly, more diffidently, and in another direction, and which often fails to work entirely. You, on the other hand, a true Kafka in strength, health, appetite, loudness of voice, eloquence, self-satisfaction, worldly dominance, endurance, presence of mind, knowledge of human nature, a certain way of doing things on a grand scale, of course also with all the defects and weaknesses that go with these advantages and into which your temperament and sometimes your hot temper drive you. You are perhaps not wholly a Kafka in your general outlook, insofar as

I can compare you with Uncle Philipp, Ludwig, and Heinrich. That is odd, and here I don't see quite clear either. After all, they were all more cheerful, fresher, more informal, more easygoing, less severe than you. (In this, by the way, I have inherited a great deal from you and taken much too good care of my inheritance, without, admittedly, having the necessary counterweights in my own nature, as you have.) Yet you too, on the other hand, have in this respect gone through various phases. You were perhaps more cheerful before you were disappointed by your children, especially by me, and were depressed at home (when other people came in, you were quite different); perhaps you have become more cheerful again since then, now that your grand-children and your son-in-law again give you something of that warmth which your children, except perhaps Valli, could not give you. In any case, we were so different and in our difference so dangerous to each other that if anyone had tried to calculate in advance how I, the slowly developing child, and you, the full-grown man, would behave toward one another, he could have assumed that you would simply trample me underfoot so that nothing was left of me. Well, that did not happen. Nothing alive can be calculated. But perhaps something worse happened. And in saying this I would all the time beg of you not to forget that I never, and not even for a single moment, believe any guilt to be on your side. The effect you had on me was the effect you could not help having. But you should stop consider-ing it some particular malice on my part that I succumbed to that effect.

I was a timid child. For all that, I am sure I was also obsti-nate, as children are. I am sure that Mother spoiled me too, but I cannot believe I was particularly difficult to manage; I cannot believe that a kindly word, a quiet taking by the hand, a friendly look, could not have got me to do anything that was wanted of me. Now you are, after all, basically a charitable and kind-hearted person (what follows will not be in contradiction to this, I am speaking only of the impression you made on the child), but not every child has the endurance and fearlessness to go on searching until it comes to the kindliness that lies beneath the surface. You can treat a child only in the way you yourself are constituted, with vigor, noise, and hot temper, and in this case such behavior seemed to you to be also most appropriate, because you wanted to bring me up to be a strong, brave boy.

Your educational methods in the very early years I can't, of course, directly describe today, but I can more or less imagine them by drawing conclusions from the later years and from your treatment of Felix. What must be considered as heightening the effect is that you were then younger and hence more energetic, wilder, more primitive, and still more reckless than you are today and that you were, besides, completely tied to the business, scarcely able to be with me even once a day, and therefore made all the more profound impression on me, one that never really leveled out to the flatness of habit.

There is only one episode in the early years of which I have a direct memory. You may remember it, too. One night I kept on whimpering for water, not, I am certain, because I was thirsty, but probably partly to be annoying, partly to amuse myself. After several vigorous threats had failed to have any effect, you took me out of bed, carried me out onto the *pavlatche*,[1] and left me there alone for a while in my nightshirt, outside the shut door. I am not going to say that this was wrong—perhaps there was really no other way of getting peace and quiet that night— but I mention it as typical of your methods of bringing up a child and their effect on me. I daresay I was quite obedient afterward at that period, but it did me inner harm. What was for me a matter of course, that senseless asking for water, and then the extraordinary terror of being carried outside were two things that I, my nature being what it was, could never properly connect with each other. Even years afterward I suffered from the tormenting fancy that the huge man, my father, the ultimate authority, would come almost for no reason at all and take me out of bed in the night and carry me out onto the *pavlatche*, and

---

1. [*Pavlatche* is the Czech word for the long balcony in the inner courtyard of old houses in Prague. —ED.]

that consequently I meant absolutely nothing as far as he was concerned.

That was only a small beginning, but this feeling of being nothing that often dominates me (a feeling that is in another respect, admittedly, also a noble and fruitful one) comes largely from your influence. What I would have needed was a little encouragement, a little friendliness, a little keeping open of my road, instead of which you blocked it for me, though of course with the good intention of making me take another road. But I was not fit for that. You encouraged me, for instance, when I saluted and marched smartly, but I was no future soldier, or you encouraged me when I was able to eat heartily or even drink beer with my meals, or when I was able to repeat songs, singing what I had not understood, or prattle to you using your own favorite expressions, imitating you, but nothing of this had anything to do with my future. And it is characteristic that even today you really only encourage me in anything when you yourself are involved in it, when what is at stake is your own sense of self-importance, which I damage (for instance by my intended marriage) or which is damaged in me (for instance when Pepa is abusive to me). Then I receive encouragement, I am reminded of my worth, the matches I would be entitled to make are pointed out to me, and Pepa is condemned utterly. But apart from the fact that at my age I am already nearly unsusceptible to encouragement, what help could it be to me anyway, if it only comes when it isn't primarily a matter of myself at all?

At that time, and at that time in every way, I would have needed encouragement. I was, after all, weighed down by your mere physical presence. I remember, for instance, how we often undressed in the same bathing hut. There was I, skinny, weakly, slight; you strong, tall, broad. Even inside the hut I felt a miserable specimen, and what's more, not only in your eyes but in the eyes of the whole world, for you were for me the measure of all things. But then when we stepped out of the bathing hut before the people, you holding me by my hand, a little skeleton, unsteady, barefoot on the boards, frightened of the water, incapable of copying your swimming strokes, which you, with the best of intentions, but actually to my profound humiliation, kept on demonstrating, then I was frantic with desperation and at such moments all my bad experiences in all areas fitted magnifi-cently together. I felt best when you sometimes undressed first and I was able to stay behind in the hut alone and put off the disgrace of showing myself in public until at last you came to see what I was doing and drove me out of the hut. I was grateful to you for not seeming to notice my anguish, and besides, I was proud of my father's body. By the way, this difference between us remains much the same to this very day.

In keeping, furthermore, was your intellectual domination. You had worked your way so far up by your own energies alone, and as a result you had unbounded confidence in your opinion. That was not yet so dazzling for me as a child as later for the boy growing up. From your armchair you ruled the world. Your opinion was correct, every other was mad, wild, meshugge, not normal. Your self-confidence indeed was so great that you had no need to be consistent at all and yet never ceased to be in the right. It did sometimes happen that you had no opinions whatsoever about a matter and as a result every conceivable opinion with respect to the matter was necessarily wrong, without exception. You were capable, for instance, of running down the Czechs, and then the Germans, and then the Jews, and what is more, not only selectively but in every respect, and finally nobody was left except yourself. For me you took on the enigmatic quality that all tyrants have whose rights are based on their person and not on reason. At least so it seemed to me.

Now, when I was the subject you were actually astonishingly often right; which in conversation was not surprising, for there was hardly ever any conversation between us, but also in reality. Yet this was nothing particularly incomprehensible, either; in all my thinking I was, after all, under the heavy pressure of your personality, even in that part of it—and particularly in that—which was not in accord with yours. All these thoughts, seemingly independent of you, were from the beginning burdened with your belittling judgments; it was almost impossible to endure this and still work out a thought with any measure of completeness and permanence. I am not here speaking of any sublime thoughts, but of every little childhood enterprise. It was only necessary to be happy about something or other, to be filled with the thought of it, to come home and speak of it, and the answer was an ironic sigh, a shaking of the head, a tapping on the table with a finger: "Is that all you're so worked up about?" or "Such worries I'd like to have!" or "The things some people have time to think about!" or "Where is that going to get you?" or "What a song and dance about nothing!" Of course, you couldn't be expected to be enthusiastic about every childish triviality when you were in a state of vexation and worry. But that was not the point. Rather, by virtue of your antagonistic nature, you could not help but always and inevitably cause the child such disappointments; and further, this antagonism, accumulating material, was constantly intensified; eventually the pattern expressed itself even if, for once, you were of the same opinion as I; finally, these disappointments of the child were not the ordinary disappointments of life but, since they involved you, the all-important personage, they struck to the very core. Courage, resolution, confidence, delight in this and that, could not last when you were against it or even if your opposition was merely to be assumed; and it was to be assumed in almost everything I did.

This applied to people as well as to thoughts. It was enough that I should take a little interest in a person—which in any case did not happen often, as a result of my nature—for you, without any consideration for my feelings or respect for my judgment, to move in with abuse, defamation, and denigration. Innocent, childlike people, such as, for instance, the Yiddish actor Löwy, had to pay for that. Without knowing him you compared him, in some dreadful way that I have now forgotten, to vermin and, as was so often the case with people I was fond of, you were automatically ready with the proverb of the dog and its fleas. Here I particularly recall the actor because at that time I made a note of your pronouncements about him, with the comment: "This is how my father speaks of my friend (whom he does not even know), simply because he is my friend. I shall always be able to bring this up against him whenever he reproaches me with the lack of a child's affection and gratitude." What was always incomprehensible to me was your total lack of feeling for the suffering and shame you could inflict on me with your words and judgments. It was as though you had no notion of your power. I too, I am sure, often hurt you with what I said, but then I always knew, and it pained me, but I could not control myself, could not keep the words back, I was sorry even while I was saying them. But you struck out with your words without much ado, you weren't sorry for anyone, either during or afterward, one was utterly defenseless against you.

But your whole method of upbringing was like that. You have, I think, a gift for bringing up children; you could, I am sure, have been of help to a human being of your own kind with your methods; such a person would have seen the reasonableness of what you told him, would not have troubled about anything else, and would quietly have done things the way he was told. But for me as a child everything you called out to me was positively a heavenly commandment, I never forgot it, it remained for me the most important means of forming a judgment of the world, above all of forming a judgment of you yourself, and there you failed entirely. Since as a child I was with you chiefly during meals, your teaching was to a large extent the teaching of proper behavior at table. What was brought to the table had to be eaten, the quality of the food was not to be discussed—but you yourself often found the food inedible, called it "this swill," said "that cow" (the cook) had ruined it. Because in accordance with your strong appetite and your particular predilection you ate everything fast, hot, and in big mouthfuls, the child had to hurry; there was a somber silence at table, interrupted by admonitions: "Eat first, talk afterward," or "Faster, faster, faster," or "There you are, you see, I finished ages ago." Bones mustn't be cracked with the teeth, but you could. Vinegar

must not be sipped noisily, but you could. The main thing was
that the bread should be cut straight. But it didn't matter that
you did it with a knife dripping with gravy. Care had to be taken
that no scraps fell on the floor. In the end it was under your chair
that there were the most scraps. At table one wasn't allowed to
do anything but eat, but you cleaned and cut your fingernails,
sharpened pencils, cleaned your ears with a toothpick. Please,
Father, understand me correctly: in themselves these would have
been utterly insignificant details, they only became depressing
for me because you, so tremendously the authoritative man, did
not keep the commandments you imposed on me. Hence the
world was for me divided into three parts: one in which I, the
slave, lived under laws that had been invented only for me and
which I could, I did not know why, never completely comply
with; then a second world, which was infinitely remote from
mine, in which you lived, concerned with government, with the
issuing of orders and with the annoyance about their not being
obeyed; and finally a third world where everybody else lived
happily and free from orders and from having to obey. I was
continually in disgrace; either I obeyed your orders, and that
was a disgrace, for they applied, after all, only to me; or I was
defiant, and that was a disgrace too, for how could I presume
to defy you; or I could not obey because I did not, for instance,
have your strength, your appetite, your skill, although you
expected it of me as a matter of course; this was the greatest disgrace of all. This was not the course of the child's reflections,
but of his feelings.

My situation at that time becomes clearer, perhaps, if I compare it with that of Felix. You do, of course, treat him in a
similar way, even indeed employing a particularly terrible
method against him in his upbringing: whenever at meals he
does anything that is in your opinion unclean, you are not content to say to him, as you used to say to me: "You are a pig,"
but add: "a real Hermann" or "just like your father." Now this
may perhaps—one can't say more than "perhaps"—not really

harm Felix in any essential way, because you are only a grand-father to him, an especially important one, of course, but still not everything as you were for me; and besides, Felix is of a quiet, even at this stage to a certain extent manly character, one who may perhaps be disconcerted by a great voice thundering at him, but not permanently conditioned by it. But above all he is, of course, only comparatively seldom with you, and besides, he is also under other influences; you are for him a rather endearing curiosity from which he can pick and choose what-ever he likes. For me you were nothing in the least like a curiosity, I couldn't pick and choose, I had to take everything.

And this without being able to produce any arguments against any of it, for it is fundamentally impossible for you to talk calmly about a subject you don't approve of or even one that was not suggested by you; your imperious temperament does not permit it. In recent years you have been explaining this as due to your nervous heart condition. I don't know that you were ever essentially different. Rather, the nervous heart condi-tion is a means by which you exert your domination more strongly, since the thought of it necessarily chokes off the least opposition from others. This is, of course, not a reproach, only a statement of fact. As in Ottla's case, when you say: "You sim-ply can't talk to her at all, she flies straight in your face," but in reality she does not begin by flying out at all. You mistake the person for the thing. The thing under discussion is what flies in your face and you immediately made up your mind about it without listening to the person; whatever is brought forward afterward merely serves to irritate you further, never to convince you. Then all one gets from you is: "Do whatever you like. So far as I'm concerned you have a free hand. You're of age, I've no advice to give you," and all this with that frightful, hoarse undertone of anger and utter condemnation that makes me tremble less today than in my childhood only because the child's exclusive sense of guilt has been partly replaced by insight into our helplessness, yours and mine.

The impossibility of getting on calmly together had one more result, actually a very natural one: I lost the capacity to talk. I daresay I would not have become a very eloquent person in any case, but I would, after all, have acquired the usual fluency of human language. But at a very early stage you forbade me to speak. Your threat, "Not a word of contradiction!" and the raised hand that accompanied it have been with me ever since. What I got from you—and you are, whenever it is a matter of your own affairs, an excellent talker—was a hesitant, stammering mode of speech, and even that was still too much for you, and finally I kept silent, at first perhaps out of defiance, and then because I could neither think nor speak in your presence. And because you were the person who really brought me up, this has had its repercussions throughout my life. It is altogether a remarkable mistake for you to believe I never complied with your wishes. "Always contrary" was really not my basic principle where you were concerned, as you believe and as you reproach me. On the contrary: if I had obeyed you less, I am sure you would have been much better pleased with me. As it is, all your educational measures hit the mark exactly. There was no hold I tried to escape. As I now am, I am (apart, of course, from the fundamentals and the influence of life itself) the result of your upbringing and of my obedience. That this result is nevertheless distressing to you, indeed that you unconsciously refuse to acknowledge it as the result of your methods of upbringing, is due to the fact that your hand and the material I offered were so alien to each other. You would say: "Not a word of contradiction!" thinking that that was a way of silencing the oppositional forces in me that were disagreeable to you, but the effect of it was too strong for me, I was too docile, I became completely dumb, cringed away from you, hid from you, and only dared to stir when I was so far away from you that your power could no longer reach me—at least not directly. But you were faced with all that, and it all seemed to you to be "contrary," whereas it was only the inevitable consequence of your strength and my weakness.

Your extremely effective rhetorical methods in bringing me up, which never failed to work with me, were: abuse, threats, irony, spiteful laughter, and—oddly enough—self-pity.

I cannot recall your ever having abused me directly and in downright abusive terms. Nor was that necessary; you had so many other methods, and besides, in talk at home and particularly at the shop the words of abuse went flying around me in such swarms, as they were flung at other people's heads, that as a little boy I was sometimes almost stunned and had no reason not to apply them to myself too, for the people you were abusing were certainly no worse than I was and you were certainly not more displeased with them than with me. And here again was your enigmatic innocence and inviolability; you cursed and swore without the slightest scruple; yet you condemned cursing and swearing in other people and would not have it.

You reinforced abusiveness with threats, and this applied to me too. How terrible for me was, for instance, that "I'll tear you apart like a fish," although I knew, of course, that nothing worse was to follow (admittedly, as a little child I didn't know that), but it was almost exactly in accord with my notions of your power, and I saw you as being capable of doing this too. It was also terrible when you ran around the table, shouting, grabbing at one, obviously not really trying to grab, yet pretending to, and Mother (finally) had to rescue one, as it seemed. Once again one had, so it seemed to the child, remained alive through your mercy and bore one's life henceforth as an undeserved gift from you. This is also the place to mention the threats about the consequences of disobedience. When I began to do something you did not like and you threatened me with the prospect of failure, my veneration for your opinion was so great that the failure became inevitable, even though perhaps it happened only at some later time. I lost confidence in my own actions. I was wavering, doubtful. The older I became, the more material there was for you to bring up against me as evidence of my worthlessness; gradually you began really to be right in a certain respect. Once again, I am careful not to assert that I became like this solely through you; you only intensified what was already there, but you intensified it greatly, simply because where I was concerned you were very powerful and you employed all your power to that end.

You put special trust in bringing up children by means of irony, and this was most in keeping with your superiority over me. An admonition from you generally took this form: "Can't you do it in such-and-such a way? That's too hard for you, I suppose. You haven't the time, of course?" and so on. And each such question would be accompanied by malicious laughter and a malicious face. One was, so to speak, already punished before one even knew that one had done something bad. Maddening were also those rebukes in which one was treated as a third person, in other words, considered not worthy even to be spoken to angrily; that is to say, when you would speak ostensibly to Mother but actually to me, who was sitting right there. For instance: "Of course, that's too much to expect of our worthy son," and the like. (This produced a corollary in that, for instance, I did not dare to ask you, and later from habit did not even really much think of asking, anything directly when Mother was there. It was much less dangerous for the child to put questions to Mother, sitting there beside you, and to ask Mother: "How is Father?"—so guarding oneself against surprises.) There were, of course, also cases when one was entirely in agreement with even the worst irony, namely, when it referred to someone else, such as Elli, with whom I was on bad terms for years. There was an orgy of malice and spiteful delight for me when such things were said of her, as they were at almost every meal: "She has to sit ten feet back from the table, the big fat lump," and when you, morosely sitting on your chair without the slightest trace of pleasantness or good humor, a bitter enemy, would exaggeratedly imitate the way she sat, which you found utterly loathsome. How often such things happened, over and over again, and how little you really achieved as a result of them! I think the reason was that the expenditure of anger and malice seemed to be in no proper relation to the subject itself, one did not have the feeling that the anger was caused by this trifle of sitting some way back from the table, but that the whole bulk of it had already been present to begin with, then, only by chance, happened to settle on this matter as a pretext for breaking out. Since one was convinced that a pretext would be found anyway, one did not try very hard, and one's feelings became dulled by these continued threats. One had gradually become pretty sure of not getting a beating, anyway. One became a glum, inattentive, disobedient child, always intent on escape, mainly within one's own self. So you suffered, and so we suffered. From your own point of view you were quite right when, clenching your teeth and with that gurgling laughter that gave the child its first notions of hell, you used to say bitterly (as you did only just recently in connection with a letter from Constantinople): "A *nice* crowd that is!"

What seemed to be quite incompatible with this attitude toward your children was, and it happened very often, that you openly lamented your situation. I confess that as a child (though probably somewhat later) I was completely callous about this and could not understand how you could possibly expect to get any sympathy from anyone. You were such a giant in every respect. What could you care for our pity or even our help? Our help, indeed, you could not but despise, as you so often despised us ourselves. Hence, I did not take these laments at their face value and looked for some hidden motive behind them. Only later did I come to understand that you really suffered a great deal because of your children; but at that time, when these laments might under different circumstances still have met with a childish, candid sympathy, unhesitatingly ready to offer any help it could, to me they had to seem like overemphatic means of disciplining me and humiliating me, as such not in themselves very intense, but with the harmful side effect that the child became conditioned not to take very seriously the very things it should have taken seriously.

Fortunately, there were exceptions to all this, mostly when you suffered in silence, and affection and kindliness by their own strength overcame all obstacles, and moved me immediately. Rare as this was, it was wonderful. For instance, in earlier years, in hot summers, when you were tired after lunch, I saw you having a nap at the office, your elbow on the desk; or you joined us in the country, in the summer holidays, on Sundays, worn out from work; or the time Mother was gravely ill and you stood holding on to the bookcase, shaking with sobs; or when, during my last illness, you came tiptoeing to Ottla's room to see me, stopping in the doorway, craning your neck to see me, and out of consideration only waved to me with your hand. At such times one would lie back and weep for happiness, and one weeps again now, writing it down.

You have a particularly beautiful, very rare way of quietly, contentedly, approvingly smiling, a way of smiling that can make the person for whom it is meant entirely happy. I can't recall its ever having expressly been my lot in my childhood, but I daresay it may have happened, for why should you have refused it to me at a time when I still seemed blameless to you and was your great hope? Yet in the long run even such friendly impressions brought about nothing but an increased sense of guilt, making the world still more incomprehensible to me.

I would rather keep to the practical and permanent. In order to assert myself even a little in relation to you, and partly too from a kind of vengefulness, I soon began to observe little ridiculous things about you, to collect them and to exaggerate them. For instance, how easily you let yourself be dazzled by people who were only seemingly above you, how you would keep on talking about them, as of some Imperial Councilor or some such (on the other hand, such things also pained me, to see you, my father, believing you had any need of such trifling confirmations of your own value, and boasting about them). Or I would note your taste for indecent expressions, which you would produce in the loudest possible voice, laughing about them as though you had said something particularly good, while in point of fact it was only a banal little obscenity (at the same time this again was for me a humiliating manifestation of your vitality). There were, of course, plenty of such observations. I was happy about them; they gave me occasion for whispering and joking; you sometimes noticed it and were angry about it, took it for malice and lack of respect, but believe me, it was for me nothing other than a means—moreover, a useless one—of attempted self-preservation; they were jokes of the kind that are made about gods and kings, jokes that are not only compatible with the profoundest respect but are indeed part and parcel of it.

Incidentally, you too, in keeping with your similar position where I was concerned, tried a similar form of self-defense. You were in the habit of pointing out how exaggeratedly well off I was and how well I had in fact been treated. That is correct, but I don't believe it was of any real use to me under the prevailing circumstances.

It is true that Mother was endlessly good to me, but for me all that was in relation to you, that is to say, in no good relation. Mother unconsciously played the part of a beater during a hunt. Even if your method of upbringing might in some unlikely case have set me on my own feet by means of producing defiance, dislike, or even hate in me, Mother canceled that out again by kindness, by talking sensibly (in the confusion of my childhood she was the very prototype of good sense and reasonableness), by pleading for me; and I was again driven back into your orbit, which I might perhaps otherwise have broken out of, to your advantage and to my own. Or it happened that no real reconciliation came about, that Mother merely shielded me from you in secret, secretly gave me something, or allowed me to do something, and then where you were concerned I was again the furtive creature, the cheat, the guilty one, who in his worthlessness could only pursue sneaky methods even to get the things he regarded as his right. Of course, I became used to taking such a course also in quest of things to which, even in my own view, I had no right. This again meant an increase in the sense of guilt.

It is also true that you hardly ever really gave me a beating. But the shouting, the way your face got red, the hasty undoing of the suspenders and laying them ready over the back of the chair, all that was almost worse for me. It is as if someone is going to be hanged. If he really is hanged, then he is dead and it is all over. But if he has to go through all the preliminaries to being hanged and he learns of his reprieve only when the noose is dangling before his face, he may suffer from it all his life. Besides, from the many occasions on which I had, according to your clearly expressed opinion, deserved a beating but was let off at the last moment by your grace, I again accumulated only a huge sense of guilt. On every side I was to blame, I was in your debt.

You have always reproached me (either alone or in front of others, since you have no feeling for the humiliation of the latter, and your children's affairs were always public) for living in peace and quiet, warmth and abundance, lacking nothing, thanks to your hard work. I think of remarks that must positively have worn grooves in my brain, such as: "When I was only seven I had to push a handcart from village to village." "We all had to sleep in one room." "We were glad when we got potatoes." "For years I had open sores on my legs because I did not have enough warm clothes." "I was only a little boy when I was sent to Pisek to work in a store." "I got nothing from home, not even when I was in the army, but still I managed to send money home." "But for all that, for all that—Father was always Father to me. Ah, nobody knows what that means these days! What do these children know? Nobody's been through that! Does any child understand such things today?" Under other conditions such stories might have been very educational, they might have been a way of encouraging one and strengthening one to endure torments and deprivations similar to those one's father had undergone. But that wasn't what you wanted at all; the situation had, after all, become quite different as a result of all your efforts, and there was no opportunity to distinguish oneself as you had done. Such an opportunity would first of all have had to be created by violence and revolutions, it would have meant breaking away from home (assuming one had had the resolution and strength to do so and that Mother wouldn't have worked against it, for her part, with other means). But that was not what you wanted at all, that you termed ingratitude, extravagance, disobedience, treachery, madness. And so, while on the one hand you tempted me to it by means of example, story, and humiliation, on the other hand you forbade it with the utmost severity. Otherwise, for instance, you ought to have been delighted with Ottla's Zürau escapade[2]—apart from the accompanying circumstances. She wanted to get back to the country from which you had come, she wanted work and hardship such as you had had, she did not want to depend on the fruits of your labor, just as you yourself were independent of your father. Were those such dreadful intentions? Was that so remote from your example and your precept? Well, Ottla's intentions finally came to nothing in practice, were indeed perhaps carried out in a somewhat ridiculous way, with too much fuss, and she did not have enough consideration for her parents. But was that exclusively her fault and not also the fault of the circumstances and, above all, of the fact that you were so estranged from her? Was she any less estranged from you (as you later tried to convince yourself) in the business than afterward at Zürau? And would you not quite certainly have had the power (assuming you could have brought yourself to do so) to turn that escapade into something very good by means of encouragement, advice, and supervision, perhaps even merely by means of toleration?

In connection with such experiences you used to say, in bitter jest, that we were too well off. But that joke is, in a sense, no joke at all. What you had to fight for we received from your hand, but the fight for external life, a fight that was instantly open to you and which we are, of course, not spared either, we now have to fight for only late in life, in our maturity but with only childish strength. I do not say that our situation is therefore inevitably less favorable than yours was, on the contrary, it is probably no better and no worse (although this is said

---

2. [Refers to his sister Ottla's taking over the management of a farm in the German-Bohemian town of Zürau. Kafka spent time with her there during his illness in 1917–18. —ED.]

without reference to our different natures), only we have the disadvantage of not being able to boast of our wretchedness and not being able to humiliate anyone with it as you have done with your wretchedness. Nor do I deny that it might have been possible for me to really enjoy the fruits of your great and successful work; that I could have turned them to good account and, to your joy, continued to work with them; but here again, our estrangement stood in the way. I could enjoy what you gave, but only in humiliation, weariness, weakness, and with a sense of guilt. That was why I could be grateful to you for everything only as a beggar is, and could never show it by doing the right things.

The next external result of this whole method of upbringing was that I fled everything that even remotely reminded me of you. First, the business. In itself, especially in my childhood, so long as it was still a simple shop, I ought to have liked it very much, it was so full of life, lit up in the evening, there was so much to see and hear; one was able to help now and then, to distinguish oneself, and, above all, to admire you for your magnificent commercial talents, for the way you sold things, managed people, made jokes, were untiring, in case of doubt knew how to make the right decision immediately, and so forth; even the way you wrapped a parcel or opened a crate was a spectacle worth watching; all this was certainly not the worst school for a child. But since you gradually began to terrify me on all sides and the business and you became one thing for me, the business too made me feel uneasy. Things that had at first been a matter of course for me there now began to torment and shame me, particularly the way you treated the staff. I don't know, perhaps it was the same in most businesses (in the Assicurazioni Generali, for instance, in my time it was really similar, and the explanation I gave the director for my resignation was, though not strictly in accordance with the truth, still not entirely a lie: my not being able to bear the cursing and swearing, which incidentally had not actually been directed at me; it was something to which I had become too painfully sensitive from home), but in my childhood other businesses did not concern me. But you I heard and saw shouting, cursing, and raging in the shop, in a way that in my opinion at that time had no equal anywhere in the world. And not only cursing, but other sorts of tyrannizing. For instance, the way you pushed goods you did not want to have mixed up with others off the counter—only the thoughtlessness of your rage was some slight excuse—and how the clerk had to pick them up. Or your constant comment about a clerk who had TB: "The sooner that sick dog croaks the better." You called the employees "paid enemies," and that was what they were, but even before they became that, you seemed to me to be their "paying enemy." There, too, I learned the great lesson that you could be unjust; in my own case I would not have noticed it so soon, for there was too much accumulated sense of guilt in me ready to admit that you were right; but in the shop, in my childish view—which later, of course, became somewhat modified, although not too much so—were strangers, who were, after all, working for us and for that reason had to live in constant dread of you. Of course I exaggerated, because I simply assumed you had as terrible an effect on these people as on me. If it had been so, they could not have lived at all; since, how-ever, they were grown-up people, most of them with excellent nerves, they shook off this abuse without any trouble and in the end it did you much more harm than it did them. But it made the business insufferable to me, reminding me far too much of my relations with you; quite apart from your proprietary interest and apart from your mania for domination even as a businessman, you were so greatly superior to all those who ever came to learn the business from you that nothing they ever did could satisfy you, and you must, as I assumed, in the same way be forever dissatisfied with me too. That was why I could not help siding with the staff; I did it also, by the way, because from sheer nervousness I could not understand how anyone could be so abusive to a stranger, and therefore—from sheer nervousness and for no other reason than my own security—I tried to reconcile the staff, which must, I thought, be in a terrible state of indignation, with you and with our family. To this end it was not enough for me to behave in an ordinary decent way toward the staff, or even modestly; more than that, I had to be humble, not only be first to say "good morning" or "good evening," but if at all possible I had to forestall any return of the greeting. And even if I, insignificant creature that I was, down below, had licked their feet it would still have been no compensation for the way that you, the master, were lashing out at them up above. This relationship that I came to have toward my fellow man extended beyond the limits of the business and on into the future (something similar, but not so dangerous and deep-going as in my case, is for instance Ottla's taste for associating with poor people, sitting together with the maids, which annoys you so much, and the like). In the end I was almost afraid of the business and, in any case, it had long ceased to be any concern of mine even before I went to the Gymnasium and hence was taken even further away from it. Besides, it seemed to be entirely beyond my resources and capacities, since, as you said, it exhausted even yours. You then tried (today this seems to me both touching and shaming) to extract, nevertheless, some little sweetness for yourself from my dislike of the business, of your work—a dislike that was after all very distressing to you—by asserting that I had no business sense, that I had loftier ideas in my head, and the like. Mother was, of course, delighted with this explanation that you wrung from yourself, and I too, in my vanity and wretchedness, let myself be influenced by it. But if it had really been only or mainly "loftier ideas" that turned me against the business (which I now, but only now, have come really and honestly to hate), they would have had to express themselves differently, instead of letting me float quickly and timidly through my schooling and my law studies until I finally landed at a clerk's desk.

If I was to escape from you, I had to escape from the family as well, even from Mother. True, one could always get protection from her, but only in relation to you. She loved you too much and was too devoted and loyal to you to have been for long an independent spiritual force in the child's struggle. This was, incidentally, a correct instinct of the child, for with the passing of the years Mother became ever more closely allied to you; while, where she herself was concerned, she always kept her independence, within the narrowest limits, delicately and beautifully, and without ever essentially hurting you, still, with the passing of the years she more and more completely, emotionally rather than intellectually, blindly adopted your judgments and your condemnations with regard to the children, particularly in the case—certainly a grave one—of Ottla. Of course, it must always be borne in mind how tormenting and utterly wearing Mother's position in the family was. She toiled in the business and in the house, and doubly suffered all the family illnesses, but the culmination of all this was what she suffered in her position between us and you. You were always affectionate and considerate toward her, but in this respect you spared her just as little as we spared her. We all hammered ruthlessly away at her, you from your side, we from ours. It was a diversion, nobody meant any harm, thinking of the battle that you were waging with us and that we were waging with you, and it was Mother who got the brunt of all our wild feelings. Nor was it at all a good contribution to the children's upbringing the way you—of course, without being in the slightest to blame for it yourself—tormented her on our account. It even seemed to justify our otherwise unjustifiable behavior toward her. How she suffered from us on your account, and from you on our account, even without counting those cases in which you were in the right because she was spoiling us, even though this "spoiling" may sometimes have been only a quiet, unconscious counterdemonstration against your system. Of course, Mother could not have borne all this if she had not drawn the strength to bear it from her love for us all and her happiness in that love.

My sisters were only partly on my side. The one who was happiest in her relation to you was Valli. Being closest to Mother, she fell in with your wishes in a similar way, without much effort and without suffering much harm. And because she reminded you of Mother, you did accept her in a more friendly spirit, although there was little Kafka material in her. But perhaps that was precisely what you wanted; where there was nothing of the Kafkas', even you could not demand anything of the sort, nor did you feel, as with the rest of us, that something was getting lost which had to be saved by force. Besides, it may be that you were never particularly fond of the Kafka element as it manifested itself in women. Valli's relationship to you would perhaps have become even friendlier if the rest of us had not disturbed it somewhat.

Elli is the only example of the almost complete success of a breaking away from your orbit. When she was a child she was the last person I should have expected it of. For she was such a clumsy, tired, timid, bad-tempered, guilt-ridden, overmeek, malicious, lazy, greedy, miserly child, I could hardly bring myself to look at her, certainly not to speak to her, so much did she remind me of myself, in so very much the same way was she under the same spell of our upbringing. Her miserliness was especially abhorrent to me, since I had it to an, if possible, even greater extent. Miserliness is, after all, one of the most reliable signs of profound unhappiness; I was so unsure of everything that, in fact, I possessed only what I actually had in my hands or in my mouth or what was at least on the way there, and this was precisely what she, being in a similar situation, most enjoyed taking away from me. But all this changed when, at an early age—this is the most important thing—she left home, married, had children, and became cheerful, carefree, brave, generous, unselfish, and hopeful. It is almost incredible how you did not really notice this change at all, or at any rate did not give it its due, blinded as you were by the grudge you have always borne Elli and fundamentally still bear her to this day; only this grudge matters much less now, since Elli no longer lives with us and, besides, your love for Felix and your affection for Karl have made it less important. Only Gerti sometimes has to suffer for it still.

I scarcely dare write of Ottla; I know that by doing so I jeopardize the whole effect I hope for from this letter. In ordinary circumstances, that is, so long as she is not in particular need or danger, all you feel is only hatred for her; you yourself have confessed to me that in your opinion she is always intentionally causing you suffering and annoyance and that while you are suffering on her account she is satisfied and pleased. In other words, a sort of fiend. What an immense estrangement, greater still than that between you and me, must have come about between you and her, for such an immense misunderstanding to be possible. She is so remote from you that you scarcely see her anymore, instead, you put a specter in the place where you suppose her to be. I grant you that you have had a particularly difficult time with her. I don't, of course, quite see to the bottom of this very complicated case, but at any rate here was something like a kind of Löwy, equipped with the best Kafka weapons. Between us there was no real struggle; I was soon finished off; what remained was flight, embitterment, melancholy, and inner struggle. But you two were always in a fighting position, always fresh, always energetic. A sight as magnificent as it was desperate. At the very beginning you were, I am sure, very close to each other, because of the four of us Ottla is even today perhaps the purest representation of the marriage between you and Mother and of the forces it combined. I don't know what it was that deprived you both of the happiness of the harmony between father and child, but I can't help believing that the development in this case was similar to that in mine. On your side there was the tyranny of your own nature, on her side the Löwy defiance, touchiness, sense of justice, restlessness, and all that backed by the consciousness of the Kafka vigor. Doubtless I too influenced her, but scarcely of my own doing, simply through the fact of my existence. Besides, as the last to arrive, she found herself in a situation in which the balance of power was already established, and was able to form her own judgment from the large amount of material at her disposal. I can even imagine that she may, in her inmost being, have wavered for some time as to whether she should fling herself into your arms or into those of the adversaries; and it is obvious that at that time there was something you failed to do and that you rebuffed her, but if it had been possible, the two of you would have become a magnificently harmonious pair. That way I should have lost an ally, but the sight of you two would have richly compensated me; besides, the incredible happiness of finding complete contentment at least in one child would have changed you much to my advantage. All this, however, is today only a dream. Ottla has no contact with her father and has to seek her way alone, like me, and the degree of confidence, self-confidence, health, and ruthlessness by which she surpasses me makes her in your eyes more wicked and treacherous than I seem to you. I understand that. From your point of view she can't be different. Indeed, she herself is capable of regarding herself with your eyes, of feeling what you suffer and of being, not desperate (despair is my business), but very sad. You do see us together often enough, in apparent contradiction to this, whispering and laughing, and now and then you hear us mentioning you. The impression you get is that of impudent conspirators. Strange conspirators. You are, admittedly, a chief subject of our conversations, as of our thoughts ever since we can remember, but truly, not in order to plot against you do we sit together, but in order to discuss—with all our might and main, jokingly and seriously, in affection, defiance, anger, revulsion, submission, consciousness of guilt, with all the resources of our heads and hearts—this terrible trial that is pending between us and you, to examine it in all its details, from all sides, on all occasions, from far and near—a trial in which you keep on claiming to be the judge, whereas, at least in the main (here I leave a margin for all the mistakes I may naturally make) you are a party too, just as weak and deluded as we are.

An example of the effect of your methods of upbringing, one that is very instructive in the context of the whole situation, is the case of Irma. On the one hand, she was, after all, a stranger, already grown up when she entered your business, and had to deal with you mainly as her employer, so that she was only partially exposed to your influence, and this at an age when she had already developed powers of resistance; yet, on the other hand, she was also a blood relation, venerating you as her father's brother, and the power you had over her was far greater than that of a mere employer. And despite all this she, who, with her frail body, was so efficient, intelligent, hard working, modest, trustworthy, unselfish, and loyal, who loved you as her uncle and admired you as her employer, she who proved herself in previous and in subsequent positions, was not a very good clerk to you. Her relationship with you was, in fact, nearly that of one of your children—pushed into that role, naturally, by us, too—and the power of your personality to bend others was, even in her case, so great that (admittedly only in relation to you and, it is to be hoped, without the deeper suffering of a child) she developed forgetfulness, carelessness, a sort of gallows humor, and perhaps even a shade of defiance, insofar as she was capable of that at all. And I do not even take into account that she was ailing, and not very happy in other respects either, and that she was burdened by a bleak home life. What was so illuminating to me in your relation to her, you yourself summed up in a remark that became classical for us, one that was almost blasphemous, but at the same time extraordinary evidence of the naïveté of your way of treating people: "The late lamented has left me quite a mess."

I might go on to describe further orbits of your influence and of the struggle against it, but there I would be entering uncertain ground and would have to construct things and, apart from that, the farther you are away from your business and your family, the pleasanter you have always become, easier to get on with, better mannered, more considerate, and more sympathetic (I mean outwardly, too), in exactly the same way as for instance an autocrat, when he happens to be outside the frontiers of his own country, has no reason to go on being tyrannical and is able to associate good-humoredly even with the lowest of the low. In fact, in the group photographs taken at Franzensbad, for instance, you always looked as big and jolly, among those sulky little people, as a king on his travels. This was something, I grant you, from which your children might have benefited too, if they had been capable of recognizing this even as little children, which was impossible; and if I, for one, had not had to live constantly within the inmost, strictest, binding ring of your influence, as, in fact, I did.

Not only did I lose my family feeling, as you say; on the contrary, I did indeed have a feeling about the family, mostly in a negative sense, concerned with the breaking away from you (which, of course, could never be done completely). Relations with people outside the family, however, suffered possibly still more under your influence. You are entirely mistaken if you believe I do everything for other people out of affection and loyalty, and for you and the family nothing, out of coldness and betrayal. I repeat for the tenth time: Even in other circumstances I should probably have become a shy and nervous person, but it is a long dark road from there to where I have really come. (Up to now I have intentionally passed over in silence relatively little in this letter, but now and later I shall have to keep silent about some things that are still too hard for me to confess—to you and to myself. I say this in order that, if the picture as a whole should be somewhat blurred here and there, you should not believe that this is due to lack of evidence; on the contrary, there is evidence that might well make the picture unbearably stark. It is not easy to find a middle way.) Here, it is enough to remind you of early days. I had lost my self-confidence where you were concerned, and in its place had developed a boundless sense of guilt. (In recollection of this boundlessness I once wrote of someone, accurately: "He is afraid the shame will outlive him.") I could not suddenly change when I was with other people; rather, I came to feel an even deeper sense of guilt with them, for, as I have already said, I had to make up to them for the wrongs you had done them in your business, wrongs in which I too had my share of responsibility. Besides, you always had some objection to make, frankly or covertly, about everyone I associated with, and for this too I had to atone. The mistrust that you tried to instill into me toward most people, at business and at home (name a single person who was of importance to me in my childhood whom you didn't at least once tear to shreds with your criticism), was, oddly enough, of no particular burden to you (you were strong enough to bear it; besides, it was perhaps really only a token of the autocrat). This mistrust (which was nowhere confirmed in the eyes of the little boy, since everywhere I saw only people excellent beyond any hope of emulation) turned in me to mistrust of myself and perpetual anxiety about everything else. There, then, I was in general certain of not being able to escape from you. That you were mistaken on this point was perhaps due to your actually never learning anything about my association with other people; and mistrustfully and jealously (I don't deny, do I, that you are fond of me?) you assumed that I had to compensate elsewhere for the lack of a family life, since it must be impossible that away from home I should live in the same way. Incidentally, in this respect, it was precisely in my childhood that I did find a certain comfort in my very mistrust of my own judgment. I would say to myself: "Oh, you're exaggerating, you tend too much to feel trivialities as great exceptions, the way young people always do." But this comfort I later lost almost entirely, when I gained a clearer perspective of the world.

I found just as little escape from you in Judaism. Here some measure of escape would have been thinkable in principle, moreover, it would have been thinkable that we might both have found each other in Judaism or that we even might have begun from there in harmony. But what sort of Judaism was it that I got from you? In the course of the years, I have taken roughly three different attitudes to it.

As a child I reproached myself, in accord with you, for not going to the synagogue often enough, for not fasting, and so on. I thought that in this way I was doing a wrong not to myself but to you, and I was penetrated by a sense of guilt, which was, of course, always near at hand.

Later, as a young man, I could not understand how, with the insignificant scrap of Judaism you yourself possessed, you could reproach me for not making an effort (for the sake of piety at least, as you put it) to cling to a similar, insignificant scrap. It was indeed, so far as I could see, a mere nothing, a joke—not even a joke. Four days a year you went to the synagogue, where you were, to say the least, closer to the indifferent than to those who took it seriously, patiently went through the prayers as a formality, sometimes amazed me by being able to show me in the prayer book the passage that was being said at the moment, and for the rest, so long as I was present in the synagogue (and this was the main thing) I was allowed to hang around wherever I liked. And so I yawned and dozed through the many hours (I don't think I was ever again so bored, except later at dancing lessons) and did my best to enjoy the few little bits of variety there were, as for instance when the Ark of the Covenant was opened, which always reminded me of the shooting galleries where a cupboard door would open in the same way whenever one hit a bull's-eye; except that there something interesting always came out and here it was always just the same old dolls without heads. Incidentally, it was also very frightening for me there, not only, as goes without saying, because of all the people one came into close contact with, but also because you once mentioned in passing that I too might be called to the Torah. That was something I dreaded for years. But otherwise I was not fundamentally disturbed in my boredom, unless it was by the bar mitzvah, but that demanded no more than some ridiculous memorizing, in other words, it led to nothing but some ridiculous passing of an examination; and, so far as you were concerned, by little, not very significant incidents, as when you were called to the Torah and passed, in what to my way of feeling was a purely social event, or when you stayed on in the synagogue for the prayers for the dead, and I was sent away, which for a long time—obviously because of the being sent away and the lack of any deeper interest—aroused in me the more or less unconscious feeling that something indecent was about to take place. That's how it was in the synagogue; at home it was, if possible, even poorer, being confined to the first Seder, which more and more developed into a farce, with fits of hysterical laughter, admittedly under the influence of the growing children. (Why did you have to give way to that influence? Because you had brought it about.) This was the religious material that was handed on to me, to which may be added at most the outstretched hand pointing to "the sons of the millionaire Fuchs," who attended the synagogue with their father on the High Holy Days. How one could do anything better with that material than get rid of it as fast as possible, I could not understand; precisely the getting rid of it seemed to me to be the devoutest action.

Still later, I did see it again differently and realized why it was possible for you to think that in this respect too I was malevolently betraying you. You really had brought some traces of Judaism with you from the ghettolike village community; it was not much and it dwindled a little more in the city and during your military service; but still, the impressions and memories of your youth did just about suffice for some sort of Jewish life, especially since you did not need much help of that kind, but came of robust stock and could personally scarcely be shaken by religious scruples unless they were strongly mixed with social scruples. Basically the faith that ruled your life consisted in your believing in the unconditional rightness of the opinions of a certain class of Jewish society, and hence actually, since these opinions were part and parcel of your own nature, in believing in yourself. Even in this there was still Judaism enough, but it was too little to be handed on to the child; it all dribbled away while you were passing it on. In part, it was youthful memories that could not be passed on to others; in part, it was your dreaded personality. It was also impossible to make a child, overacutely observant from sheer nervousness, understand that the few flimsy gestures you performed in the name of Judaism, and with an indifference in keeping with their flimsiness, could have any higher meaning. For you they had meaning as little souvenirs of earlier times, and that was why you wanted to pass them on to me, but since they no longer had any intrinsic value even for you, you could do this only through persuasion or threat; on the one hand, this could not be successful, and on the other, it had to make you very angry with me on account of my apparent obstinacy, since you did not recognize the weakness of your position in this.

The whole thing is, of course, no isolated phenomenon. It was much the same with a large section of this transitional generation of Jews, which had migrated from the still comparatively devout countryside to the cities. It happened automatically; only, it added to our relationship, which certainly did not lack in acrimony, one more sufficiently painful source for it. Although you ought to believe, as I do, in your guiltlessness in this matter too, you ought to explain this guiltlessness by your nature and by the conditions of the times, not merely by external circumstances; that is, not by saying, for instance, that you had too much work and too many other worries to be able to bother with such things as well. In this manner you tend to twist your undoubted guiltlessness into an unjust reproach to others. That can be very easily refuted everywhere and here too. It was not a matter of any sort of instruction you ought to have given your children, but of an exemplary life. Had your Judaism been stronger, your example would have been more compelling too; this goes without saying and is, again, by no means a reproach, but only a refutation of your reproaches. You have recently been reading Franklin's memoirs of his youth. I really did purposely give you this book to read, though not, as you ironically commented, because of a little passage on vegetarianism, but because of the relationship between the author and his father, as it is there described, and of the relationship between the author and his son, as it is spontaneously revealed in these memoirs written for that son. I do not wish to dwell here on matters of detail.

I have received a certain retrospective confirmation of this view of your Judaism from your attitude in recent years, when it seemed to you that I was taking more interest in Jewish matters. As you have in advance an aversion to every one of my activities and especially to the nature of my interest, so you have had it here too. But in spite of this, one could have expected that in this case you would make a little exception. It was, after all, Judaism of your Judaism that was coming to life here, and with it also the possibility of entering into a new relationship between us. I do not deny that, had you shown interest in them, these things might, for that very reason, have become suspect in my eyes. I do not even dream of asserting that I am in this respect any better than you are. But it never came to the test. Through my intervention Judaism became abhorrent to you, Jewish writings unreadable; they "nauseated" you. This may have meant you insisted that only that Judaism which you had shown me in my childhood was the right one, and beyond it there was nothing. Yet that you should insist on it was really hardly thinkable. But then the "nausea" (apart from the fact that it was directed primarily not against Judaism but against me personally) could only mean that unconsciously you did acknowledge the weakness of your Judaism and of my Jewish upbringing, did not wish to be reminded of it in any way, and reacted to any reminder with frank hatred. Incidentally, your negative high esteem of my new Judaism was much exaggerated; first of all, it bore your curse within it, and secondly, in its development the fundamental relationship to one's fellow men was decisive, in my case that is to say fatal.

You struck closer to home with your aversion to my writing and to everything that, unknown to you, was connected with it. Here I had, in fact, got some distance away from you by my own efforts, even if it was slightly reminiscent of the worm that, when a foot treads on its tail end, breaks loose with its front part and drags itself aside. To a certain extent I was in safety; there was a chance to breathe freely. The aversion you naturally and immediately took to my writing was, for once, welcome to me. My vanity, my ambition did suffer under your soon proverbial way of hailing the arrival of my books: "Put it on my bedside table!" (usually you were playing cards when a book came), but I was really quite glad of it, not only out of rebellious malice, not only out of delight at a new confirmation of my view of our relationship, but quite spontaneously, because to me that formula sounded something like: "Now you are free!" Of course it was a delusion; I was not, or, to put it most optimistically, was not yet, free. My writing was all about you; all I did there, after all, was to bemoan what I could not bemoan upon your breast. It was an intentionally long and drawn-out leave-taking from you, yet, although it was enforced by you, it did take its course in the direction determined by me. But how little all this amounted to! It is only worth talking about because it happened in my life, otherwise it would not even be noted; and also because in my childhood it ruled my life as a premonition, later as a hope, and still later often as despair, and it dictated—yet again in your shape, it may be said—my few small decisions.

For instance, the choice of a career. True, here you gave me complete freedom, in your magnanimous and, in this regard, even indulgent manner. Although here again you were conforming to the general method of treating sons in the Jewish middle class, which was the standard for you, or at least to the values of that class. Finally, one of your misunderstandings concerning my person played a part in this too. In fact, out of paternal pride, ignorance of my real life, and conclusions drawn from my feebleness, you have always regarded me as particularly diligent. As a child I was, in your view, always studying, and later always writing. This does not even remotely correspond to the facts. It would be more correct, and much less exaggerated, to say that I studied little and learned nothing; that something did stick in my mind after those many years is, after all, not very remarkable, since I did have a moderately good memory and a not too inferior capacity for learning; but the sum total of knowledge and especially of a solid grounding of knowledge is extremely pitiable in comparison with the expenditure of time and money in the course of an outwardly untroubled, calm life, particularly also in comparison with almost all the people I know. It is pitiable, but to me understandable. Ever since I could think, I have had such profound anxieties about asserting my spiritual and intellectual existence that I was indifferent to everything else. Jewish schoolboys in our country often tend to be odd; among them one finds the most unlikely things; but something like my cold indifference, scarcely disguised, indestructible, childishly helpless, approaching the ridiculous, and brutishly complacent, the indifference of a self-sufficient but coldly imaginative child, I have never found anywhere else; to be sure, it was the sole defense against destruction of the nerves by fear and by a sense of guilt. All that occupied my mind was worry about myself, and this in various ways. There was, for instance, the worry about my health; it began imperceptibly enough, with now and then a little anxiety about digestion, hair falling out, a spinal curvature, and so on; intensifying in innumerable gradations, it finally ended with a real illness. But since there was nothing at all I was certain of, since I needed to be provided at every instant with a new confirmation of my existence, since nothing was in my very own, undoubted, sole possession, determined unequivocally only by me—in sober truth a disinherited son—naturally I became unsure even to the thing nearest to me, my own body. I shot up, tall and lanky, without knowing what to do with my lankiness, the burden was too heavy, the back became bent; I scarcely dared to move, certainly not to exercise, I remained weakly; I was amazed by everything I could still command as by a miracle, for instance, my good digestion; that sufficed to lose it, and now the way was open to every sort of hypochondria; until finally under the strain of the superhuman effort of wanting to marry (of this I shall speak later), blood came from the lung, something in which the apartment in the Schönbornpalais—which, however, I needed only because I believed I needed it for my writing, so that even this belongs here under the same heading—may have had a fair share. So all this did not come from excessive work, as you always imagine. There were years in which, in perfectly good health, I lazed away more time on the sofa than you in all your life, including all your illnesses. When I rushed away from you, frightfully busy, it was generally in order to lie down in my room. My total achievement in work done, both at the office (where laziness is, of course, not particularly striking, and besides, mine was kept in bounds by my anxiety) and at home, is minute; if you had any real idea of it, you would be aghast. Probably I am constitutionally not lazy at all, but there was nothing for me to do. In the place where I lived I was spurned, condemned, fought to a standstill; and to escape to some other place was an enormous exertion, but that was not work, for it was something impossible, something that was, with small exceptions, unattainable for me.

This was the state in which I was given the freedom of choice of a career. But was I still capable of making any use of such freedom? Had I still any confidence in my own capacity to achieve a real career? My valuation of myself was much more dependent on you than on anything else, such as some external success. *That* was strengthening for a moment, nothing more, but on the other side your weight always dragged me down much more strongly. Never shall I pass the first grade in grammar school, I thought, but I succeeded, I even got a prize; but I shall certainly not pass the entrance exam for the Gymnasium, but I succeeded; but now I shall certainly fail in the first year at the Gymnasium; no, I did not fail, and I went on and on succeeding. This did not produce any confidence, however; on the contrary, I was always convinced—and I had positive proof of it in your forbidding expression—that the more I achieved, the worse the final outcome would inevitably be. Often in my mind's eye I saw the terrible assembly of the teachers (the Gymnasium is only the most obvious example, but it was the same all around me), as they would meet, when I had passed the first class, and then in the second class, when I had passed that, and then in the third, and so on, meeting in order to examine this unique, outrageous case, to discover how I, the most incapable, or at least the most ignorant of all, had succeeded in creeping up so far as this class, which now, when everybody's attention had at last been focused on me, would of course instantly spew me out, to the jubilation of all the righteous liberated from this nightmare. To live with such fantasies is not easy for a child. In these circumstances, what could I care about my lessons? Who was able to strike a spark of real interest in me? Lessons, and not only lessons but everything around me, interested me as much, at that decisive age, as an embezzling bank clerk, still holding his job and trembling at the thought of discovery, is interested in the petty ongoing business of the bank, which he still has to deal with as a clerk. That was how small and faraway everything was in comparison to the main thing. So it went on up to the qualifying exams which I really passed partly only through cheating, and then everything came to a standstill, for now I was free. If I had been concerned only with myself up to now, despite the discipline of the Gymnasium, how much more so now that I was free. So there was actually no such thing for me as freedom to choose my career, for I knew: compared to the main thing everything would be exactly as much a matter of indifference to me as all the subjects taught at school, and so it was a matter of finding a profession that would let me indulge this indifference without injuring my vanity too much. Law was the obvious choice. Little contrary attempts on the part of vanity, of senseless hope, such as a fortnight's study of chemistry, or six months' German studies, only reinforced that fundamental conviction. So I studied law. This meant that in the few months before the exams, and in a way that told severely on my nerves, I was positively living, in an intellectual sense, on sawdust, which had moreover already been chewed for me in thousands of other people's mouths. But in a certain sense this was exactly to my taste, as in a certain sense the Gymnasium had been earlier, and later my job as a clerk, for it all suited my situation. At any rate, I did show astonishing foresight; even as a small child I had had fairly clear premonitions about my studies and my career. From this side I did not expect rescue; here I had given up long ago.

But I showed no foresight at all concerning the significance and possibility of a marriage for me; this up to now greatest terror of my life has come upon me almost completely unexpectedly. The child had developed so slowly, these things were outwardly all too remote; now and then the necessity of thinking of them did arise; but the fact that here a permanent, decisive, and indeed the most grimly bitter ordeal loomed was impossible to recognize. In reality, however, the marriage plans turned out to be the most grandiose and hopeful attempts at escape, and, consequently, their failure was correspondingly grandiose.

I am afraid that, because in this sphere everything I try is a failure, I shall also fail to make these attempts to marry comprehensible to you. And yet the success of this whole letter depends on it, for in these attempts there was, on the one hand, concentrated everything I had at my disposal in the way of positive forces, and, on the other hand, there also accumulated, and with downright fury, all the negative forces that I have described as being the result in part of your method of upbringing, that is to say, the weakness, the lack of self-confidence, the sense of guilt, and they positively drew a cordon between myself and marriage. The explanation will be hard for me also because I have spent so many days and nights thinking and burrowing through the whole thing over and over again that now even I myself am bewildered by the mere sight of it. The only thing that makes the explanation easier for me is your—in my opinion—complete misunderstanding of the matter; to correct slightly so complete a misunderstanding does not seem excessively difficult.

First of all you rank the failure of the marriages with the rest of my failures; I should have nothing against this, provided you accepted my previous explanation of my failure as a whole. It does, in fact, form part of the same series, only you underrate the importance of the matter, underrating it to such an extent that whenever we talk of it we are actually talking about quite different things. I venture to say that nothing has happened to you in your whole life that had such importance for you as the attempts at marriage have had for me. By this I do not mean that you have not experienced anything in itself as important;— on the contrary, your life was much richer and more careladen and more concentrated than mine, but for that very reason nothing of this sort has happened to you. It is as if one person had to climb five low steps and another person only one step, but one that is, at least for him, as high as all the other five put together; the first person will not only manage the five, but hundreds and thousands more as well, he will have led a great and very strenuous life, but none of the steps he has climbed will have been of such importance to him as for the second person that one, first, high step, that step which it is impossible for him to climb even by exerting all his strength, that step which he cannot get up on and which he naturally cannot get past either.

Marrying, founding a family, accepting all the children that come, supporting them in this insecure world and perhaps even guiding them a little, is, I am convinced, the utmost a human being can succeed in doing at all. That so many seem to succeed in this is no evidence to the contrary; first of all, there are not many who do succeed, and second, these not-many usually don't "do" it, it merely "happens" to them; although this is not that *utmost,* it is still very great and very honorable (particularly since "doing" and "happening" cannot be kept clearly distinct). And finally, it is not a matter of this Utmost at all, anyway, but only of some distant but decent approximation; it is, after all, not necessary to fly right into the middle of the sun, but it is necessary to crawl to a clean little spot on Earth where the sun sometimes shines and one can warm oneself a little.

How was I prepared for this? As badly as possible. This is apparent from what has been said up to now. Insofar as any direct preparation of the individual and any direct creation of the general basic conditions exist, you did not intervene much outwardly. And it could not be otherwise; what is decisive here are the general sexual customs of class, nation, and time. Yet you did intervene here too—not much, for such intervention must presuppose great mutual trust, and both of us had been lacking in this even long before the decisive time came—and not very happily, because our needs were quite different; what grips me need hardly touch you at all, and vice versa; what is innocence in you may be guilt in me, and vice versa; what has no consequences for you may be the last nail in my coffin.

I remember going for a walk one evening with you and Mother; it was on Josephsplatz near where the Länderbank is today; and I began talking about these interesting things, in a stupidly boastful, superior, proud, detached (that was spurious), cold (that was genuine), and stammering manner, as indeed I usually talked to you, reproaching the two of you with having left me uninstructed; with the fact that my schoolmates first had to take me in hand, that I had been close to great dangers (here I was brazenly lying, as was my way, in order to show myself brave, for as a consequence of my timidity I had, except for the usual sexual misdemeanors of city children, no very exact notion of these "great dangers"); but finally I hinted that now, fortunately, I knew everything, no longer needed any advice, and that everything was all right. I had begun talking about all this mainly because it gave me pleasure at least to talk about it, and also out of curiosity, and finally to avenge myself somehow on the two of you for something or other. In keeping with your nature you took it quite simply, only saying something to the effect that you could give me advice about how I could go in for these things without danger. Perhaps I did want to lure just such an answer out of you; it was in keeping with the prurience of a child overfed with meat and all good things, physically inactive, everlastingly occupied with himself; but still, my outward sense of shame was so hurt by this—or I believed it ought to be so hurt—that against my will I could not go on talking to you about it and, with arrogant impudence, cut the conversation short.

It is not easy to judge the answer you gave me then; on the one hand, it had something staggeringly frank, sort of primeval, about it; on the other hand, as far as the lesson itself is concerned, it was uninhibited in a very modern way. I don't know how old I was at the time, certainly not much over sixteen. It was, nevertheless, a very remarkable answer for such a boy, and the distance between the two of us is also shown in the fact that it was actually the first direct instruction bearing on real life I ever received from you. Its real meaning, however, which sank into my mind even then, but which came partly to the surface of my consciousness only much later, was this: what you advised me to do was in your opinion and even more in my opinion at that time, the filthiest thing possible. That you wanted to see to it that I should not bring any of the physical filth home with me was unimportant, for you were only protecting yourself, your house. The important thing was rather that you yourself remained outside your own advice, a married man, a pure man, above such things; this was probably intensified for me at the time by the fact that even marriage seemed to me shameless; and hence it was impossible for me to apply to my parents the general information I had picked up about marriage. Thus you became still purer, rose still higher. The thought that you might have given yourself similar advice before your marriage was to me utterly unthinkable. So there was hardly any smudge of earthly filth on you at all. And it was you who pushed me down into this filth—just as though I were predestined to it—with a few frank words. And so, if the world consisted only of me and you (a notion I was much inclined to have), then this purity of the world came to an end with you and, by virtue of your advice, the filth began with me. In itself it was, of course, incomprehensible that you should thus condemn me; only old guilt, and profoundest contempt on your side, could explain it to me. And so again I was seized in my innermost being—and very hard indeed.

Here perhaps both our guiltlessness becomes most evident. A gives B a piece of advice that is frank, in keeping with his attitude toward life, not very lovely but still, even today, perfectly usual in the city, a piece of advice that might prevent damage to health. This piece of advice is for B morally not very invigorating—but why should he not be able to work his way out of it, and repair the damage in the course of the years? Besides, he does not even have to take the advice; and there is no reason why the advice itself should cause B's whole future world to come tumbling down. And yet something of this kind does happen, but only for the very reason that A is you and B is myself.

This guiltlessness on both sides I can judge especially well because a similar clash between us occurred some twenty years later, in quite different circumstances—horrible in itself but much less damaging—for what was there in me, the thirty-six year old, that could still be damaged? I am referring to a brief discussion on one of those few tumultuous days that followed the announcement of my latest marriage plans. You said to me something like this: "She probably put on a fancy blouse, something these Prague Jewesses are good at, and right away, of course, you decided to marry her. And that as fast as possible, in a week, tomorrow, today. I can't understand you: after all, you're a grown man, you live in the city, and you don't know what to do but marry the first girl who comes along. Isn't there anything else you can do? If you're frightened, I'll go with you." You put it in more detail and more plainly, but I can no longer recall the details, perhaps too things became a little vague before my eyes, I paid almost more attention to Mother who, though in complete agreement with you, took something from the table and left the room with it.

You have hardly ever humiliated me more deeply with words and shown me your contempt more clearly. When you spoke to me in a similar way twenty years earlier, one might, looking at it through your eyes, have seen in it some respect for the precocious city boy, who in your opinion could already be initiated into life without more ado. Today this consideration could only intensify the contempt, for the boy who was about to make his first start got stuck halfway and today does not seem richer by any experience, only more pitiable by twenty years. My choice of a girl meant nothing at all to you. You had (unconsciously) always suppressed my power of decision and now believed (unconsciously) that you knew what it was worth. Of my attempts at escape in other directions you knew nothing, thus you could not know anything either of the thought processes that had led me to this attempt to marry, and had to try to guess at them, and in keeping with your general opinion of me, you interpreted them in the most abominable, crude, and ridiculous light. And you did not for a moment hesitate to tell me this in just such a manner. The shame you inflicted on me with this was nothing to you in comparison to the shame that I would, in your opinion, inflict on your name by this marriage.

Now, regarding my attempts at marriage there is much you can say in reply, and you have indeed done so: you could not have much respect for my decision since I had twice broken the engagement with F. and had twice renewed it, since I had needlessly dragged you and Mother to Berlin to celebrate the engagement, and the like. All this is true—but how did it come about?

The fundamental thought behind both attempts at marriage was quite sound: to set up house, to become independent. An idea that does appeal to you, only in reality it always turns out like the children's game in which one holds and even grips the other's hand, calling out: "Oh, go away, go away, why don't you go away?" Which in our case happens to be complicated by the fact that you have always honestly meant this "go away!" and have always unknowingly held me, or rather held me down, only by the strength of your personality.

Although both girls were chosen by chance, they were extraordinarily well chosen. Again a sign of your complete misunderstanding, that you can believe that I—timid, hesitant, suspicious—can decide to marry in a flash, out of delight over a blouse. Both marriages would rather have been commonsense marriages, insofar as that means that day and night—the first time for years, the second time for months—all my power of thought was concentrated on the plan.

Neither of the girls disappointed me, only I disappointed both of them. My opinion of them is today exactly the same as when I wanted to marry them.

It is not true either that in my second marriage attempt I disregarded the experience gained from the first attempt, that I was rash and careless. The cases were quite different; precisely the earlier experience held out a hope for the second case, which was altogether much more promising. I do not want to go into details here.

Why then did I not marry? There were certainly obstacles, as there always are, but then, life consists in confronting such obstacles. The essential obstacle, however, which is, unfortunately, independent of the individual case, is that obviously I am mentally incapable of marrying. This manifests itself in the fact that from the moment I make up my mind to marry I can no longer sleep, my head burns day and night, life can no longer be called life, I stagger about in despair. It is not actually worries that bring this about; true, in keeping with my sluggishness and pedantry countless worries are involved in all this, but they are not decisive; they do, like worms, complete the work on the corpse, but the decisive blow has come from elsewhere. It is the general pressure of anxiety, of weakness, of self-contempt.

I will try to explain it in more detail. Here, in the attempt to marry, two seemingly antagonistic elements in my relations with you unite more intensely than anywhere else. Marriage certainly is the pledge of the most acute form of self-liberation and independence. I would have a family, in my opinion the highest one can achieve, and so too the highest you have achieved; I would be your equal; all old and ever new shame and tyranny would be mere history. It would be like a fairy tale, but precisely there lies the questionable element. It is too much; so much cannot be achieved. It is as if a person were a prisoner, and he had not only the intention to escape, which would perhaps be attainable, but also, and indeed simultaneously, the intention to rebuild the prison as a pleasure dome for himself. But if he escapes, he cannot rebuild, and if he rebuilds, he cannot escape. If I, in the particular unhappy relationship in which I stand to you, want to become independent, I must do something that will have, if possible, no connection with you at all;

though marrying is the greatest thing of all and provides the most honorable independence, it also stands at the same time in the closest relation to you. To try to get out of this quandary has therefore a touch of madness about it, and every attempt is punished by being driven almost mad.

It is precisely this close relation that partly lures me toward marrying. I picture the equality which would then arise between us—and which you would be able to understand better than any other form of equality—as so beautiful because then I could be a free, grateful, guiltless, upright son, and you could be an untroubled, untyrannical, sympathetic, contented father. But to this end everything that ever happened would have to be undone, that is, we ourselves should have to be canceled out.

But we being what we are, marrying is barred to me because it is your very own domain. Sometimes I imagine the map of the world spread out and you stretched diagonally across it. And I feel as if I could consider living in only those regions that either are not covered by you or are not within your reach. And, in keeping with the conception I have of your magnitude, these are not many and not very comforting regions—and marriage is not among them.

This very comparison proves that I certainly do not mean to say that you drove me away from marriage by your example, as you had driven me away from your business. Quite the contrary, despite the remote similarity. In your marriage I had before me what was, in many ways, a model marriage, a model in constancy, mutual help, number of children; and even when the children grew up and increasingly disturbed the peace, the marriage as such remained undisturbed. Perhaps I formed my high idea of marriage on this model; the desire for marriage was powerless for other reasons. Those lay in your relation to your children, which is, after all, what this whole letter is about.

There is a view according to which fear of marriage sometimes has its source in a fear that one's children would some day pay one back for the sins one has committed against one's own parents. This, I believe, has no very great significance in my case, for my sense of guilt actually originates in you, and is filled with such conviction of its uniqueness—indeed, this feeling of uniqueness is an essential part of its tormenting nature—that any repetition is unthinkable. All the same, I must say that I would find such a mute, glum, dry, doomed son unbearable; I daresay that, if there were no other possibility, I would flee from him, emigrate, as you had planned to do if I had married. And this may also have had some influence on my incapacity to marry.

What is much more important in all this, however, is the anxiety about myself. This has to be understood as follows: I have already indicated that in my writing, and in everything connected with it, I have made some attempts at independence, attempts at escape, with the very smallest of success; they will scarcely lead any farther; much confirms this for me. Nevertheless it is my duty or, rather, the essence of my life, to watch over them, to let no danger that I can avert, indeed no possibility of such a danger, approach them. Marriage bears the possibility of such a danger, though also the possibility of the greatest help; for me, however, it is enough that there is the possibility of a danger. What should I do if it did turn out to be a danger! How could I continue living in matrimony with the perhaps unprovable, but nevertheless irrefutable feeling that this danger existed? Faced with this I may waver, but the final outcome is certain: I must renounce. The simile of the bird in the hand and the two in the bush has only a very remote application here. In my hand I have nothing, in the bush is everything, and yet—so it is decided by the conditions of battle and the exigency of life—I must choose the nothing. I had to make a similar choice when I chose my profession.

The most important obstacle to marriage, however, is the no longer eradicable conviction that what is essential to the support of a family and especially to its guidance, is what I have recognized in you; and indeed everything rolled into one, good and bad, as it is organically combined in you—strength, and scorn of others, health, and a certain immoderation, eloquence and inadequacy, self-confidence and dissatisfaction with everyone else, a worldly wisdom and tyranny, knowledge of human nature and mistrust of most people; then also good qualities without any drawback, such as industry, endurance, presence of mind, and fearlessness. By comparison I had almost nothing or very little of all this; and was it on this basis that I wanted to risk marrying, when I could see for myself that even you had to fight hard in marriage and, where the children were concerned, had even failed? Of course, I did not put this question to myself in so many words and I did not answer it in so many words; otherwise everyday thinking would have taken over and shown me other men who are different from you (to name one, near at hand, who is very different from you: Uncle Richard) and yet have married and have at least not collapsed under the strain, which is in itself a great deal and would have been quite enough for me. But I did not ask this question, I lived it from childhood on. I tested myself not only when faced with marriage, but in the face of every trifle; in the face of every trifle you by your example and your method of upbringing convinced me, as I have tried to describe, of my incapacity; and what turned out to be true of every trifle and proved you right, had to be fearfully true of the greatest thing of all: of marriage. Up to the time of my marriage attempts I grew up more or less like a businessman who lives from day to day, with worries and forebodings, but without keeping proper accounts. He makes a few small profits—which he constantly pampers and exaggerates in his imagination because of their rarity—but otherwise he has daily losses. Everything is entered, but never balanced. Now comes the necessity of drawing a balance, that is, the attempt at marriage. And with the large sums that have to be taken into account here it is as though there had never been even the smallest profit, everything one single great liability. And now marry without going mad!

That is what my life with you has been like up to now, and these are the prospects inherent in it for the future.

If you look at the reasons I offer for the fear I have of you, you might answer: "You maintain I make things easy for myself by explaining my relation to you simply as being your fault, but I believe that despite your outward effort, you do not make things more difficult for yourself, but much more profitable. At first you too repudiate all guilt and responsibility; in this our methods are the same. But whereas I then attribute the sole guilt to you as frankly as I mean it, you want to be 'overly clever' and 'overly affectionate' at the same time and acquit me also of all guilt. Of course, in the latter you only seem to succeed (and more you do not even want), and what appears between the lines, in spite of all the 'turns of phrase' about character and nature and antagonism and helplessness, is that actually I have been the aggressor, while everything you were up to was self-defense. By now you would have achieved enough by your very insincerity, for you have proved three things: first, that you are not guilty; second, that I am the guilty one; and third, that out of sheer magnanimity you are ready not only to forgive me but (what is both more and less) also to prove and be willing to believe yourself that—contrary to the truth—I also am not guilty. That ought to be enough for you now, but it is still not enough. You have put it into your head to live entirely off me. I admit that we fight with each other, but there are two kinds of combat. The chivalrous combat, in which independent opponents pit their strength against each other, each on his own, each losing on his own, each winning on his own. And there is the combat of vermin, which not only sting but, on top of it, suck your blood in order to sustain their own life. That's what the real professional soldier is, and that's what you are. You are unfit for life; to make life comfortable for yourself, without worries and without self-reproaches, you prove that I have taken your fitness for life away from you and put it in my own pocket. Why should it bother you that you are unfit for life, since I have the responsibility for it, while you calmly stretch out and let yourself be hauled through life, physically and mentally, by me. For example: when you recently wanted to marry, you wanted—and this you do, after all, admit in this letter—at the same time not to marry, but in order not to have to exert yourself you wanted me to help you with this not-marrying, by forbidding this marriage because of the 'disgrace' this union would bring upon my name. I did not dream of it. First, in this as in everything else I never wanted to be 'an obstacle to your happiness,' and second, I never want to have to hear such a reproach from my child. But did the self-restraint with which I left the marriage up to you do me any good? Not in the least. My aversion to your marriage would not have prevented it; on the contrary, it would have been an added incentive for you to marry the girl, for it would have made the 'attempt at escape,' as you put it, complete. And my consent to your marriage did not prevent your reproaches, for you prove that I am in any case to blame for your not marrying. Basically, however, in this as in everything else you have only proved to me that all my reproaches were justified, and that one especially justified charge was still missing: namely, the charge of insincerity, obsequiousness, and parasitism. If I am not very much mistaken, you are preying on me even with this letter itself."

My answer to this is that, after all, this whole rejoinder—which can partly also be turned against you—does not come from you, but from me. Not even your mistrust of others is as great as my self-mistrust, which you have bred in me. I do not deny a certain justification for this rejoinder, which in itself contributes new material to the characterization of our relationship. Naturally things cannot in reality fit together the way the evidence does in my letter; life is more than a Chinese puzzle. But with the correction made by this rejoinder—a correction I neither can nor will elaborate in detail—in my opinion something has been achieved which so closely approximates the truth that it might reassure us both a little and make our living and our dying easier. ༄

FRANZ

The Judgment

I T WAS A Sunday morning at the very height of spring. Georg Bendemann, a young merchant, was sitting in his own room on the second floor of one of a long row of low, graceful houses stretching along the bank of the river, distinguishable from one another only in height and color. He had just finished a letter to an old friend who was now living abroad, had sealed it in its envelope with slow and dreamy deliberateness, and with one elbow propped on his desk was looking out the window at the river, the bridge, and the hills on the farther bank with their tender green.

He was thinking about this friend, who years before had simply run off to Russia, dissatisfied with his prospects at home. Now he was running a business in St. Petersburg, which at first had flourished but more recently seemed to be going downhill, as the friend always complained on his increasingly rare visits. So there he was, wearing himself out to no purpose in a foreign country; the exotic-looking beard he wore did not quite conceal the face Georg had known so well since childhood, and the jaundice color his skin had begun to take on seemed to signal the onset of some disease. By his own account he had no real contact with the colony of his fellow countrymen there and almost no social connection with Russian families, so that he was resigning himself to life as a confirmed bachelor.

What could one write to such a man, who had obviously gone badly astray, a man one could be sorry for but not help? Should one perhaps advise him to come home, to reestablish himself here and take up his old friendships again—there was certainly nothing to stand in the way of that—and in general to rely on the help of his friends? But that was as good as telling him—and the more kindly it was done the more he would take offense—that all his previous efforts had miscarried, that he should finally give up, come back home, and be gaped at by everyone as a returned prodigal, that only his friends knew what was what, and that he himself was nothing more than a big child and should follow the example of his friends who had stayed at home and become successful. And besides, was it certain that all the pain they would necessarily inflict on him would serve any purpose? Perhaps it would not even be possible to get him to come home at all—he said himself that he was now out of touch with business conditions in his native country—and then he would still be left an alien in an alien land, embittered by his friends' advice and more than ever estranged from them. But if he did follow their advice and even then didn't fit in at home—not because of the malice of others, of course, but through sheer force of circumstances—if he couldn't get on with his friends or without them, felt humiliated, couldn't really be said to have either friends or a country of his own any longer, wouldn't it be better for him to go on living abroad just as he was? Taking all this into account, how could one expect that he would make a success of life back here?

For such reasons, assuming one wanted to keep up any correspondence with him at all, one could not send him the sort of real news one could frankly tell the most casual acquaintances. It had been more than three years since his last visit, and for this he offered the lame excuse that the political situation in Russia was too uncertain and apparently would not permit even the briefest absence of a small businessman, though it allowed hundreds of thousands of Russians to travel the globe in perfect safety. But during these same three years Georg's own position in life had changed considerably. Two years ago his mother had died and since then he and his father had shared the household together; and his friend had, of course, been informed of that and had expressed his sympathy in a letter phrased so dryly that the grief normally caused by such an event, one had to conclude, could not be comprehended so far away from home. Since that time, however, Georg had applied himself with greater determination to his business as well as to everything else. Perhaps it was his father's insistence on having everything his own way in the business that had prevented him, during his mother's lifetime, from pursuing any real projects of his own; perhaps since her death his father had become less aggressive, although he was still active in the business; perhaps it was mostly due to an accidental run of good fortune—that was very probable indeed—but, at any rate, during those two years the business had prospered most unexpectedly, the staff had to be doubled, the volume was five times as great; no doubt about it, further progress lay just ahead.

But Georg's friend had no inkling of these changes. In earlier years, perhaps for the last time in that letter of condolence, he had tried to persuade Georg to emigrate to Russia and had enlarged upon the prospects of success in St. Petersburg for precisely Georg's line of business. The figures quoted were microscopic by comparison with Georg's present operations. Yet he shrank from letting his friend know about his business success, and if he were to do so now—retrospectively—that certainly would look peculiar.

So Georg confined himself to giving his friend unimportant items of gossip such as rise at random in the memory when one is idly thinking things over on a quiet Sunday. All he desired was to leave undisturbed the image of the hometown which his friend had most likely built up and accepted during his long absence. And thus it happened that three times in three fairly widely separated letters Georg had told his friend about the engagement of some insignificant man to an equally insignificant girl, until, quite contrary to Georg's intentions, his friend actually began to show some interest in this notable event.

Yet Georg much preferred to write about things like these rather than to confess that he himself had become engaged a month ago to a Fräulein Frieda Brandenfeld, a girl from a well-to-do family. He often spoke to his fiancée about this friend of his and the peculiar relationship that had developed between them in their correspondence. "Then he won't be coming to our wedding," she said, "and yet I have a right to get to know all your friends." "I don't want to trouble him," answered Georg, "don't misunderstand, he would probably come, at least I think so, but he would feel that his hand had been forced and he would be hurt, perhaps he would even envy me and certainly he'd be discontented, and without ever being able to do anything about his discontent he'd have to go away again alone. Alone—do you know what that means?" "Yes, but what if he hears about our marriage from some other source?" "I can't prevent that, of course, but it's unlikely, considering the way he lives." "If you have friends like that, Georg, you shouldn't ever have gotten engaged at all." "Well, we're both to blame for that; but I wouldn't have it any other way now." And when, breathing heavily under his kisses, she was still able to add, "All the same, it does upset me," he thought it would not really do any harm if he were to send the news to his friend. "That's the kind of man I am and he'll just have to accept me or not," he said to himself, "I can't cut myself to another pattern that might make a more suitable friend for him."

And, in fact, he did inform his friend about his engagement, in the long letter he had been writing that Sunday morning, with the following words: "I have saved up my best news for last. I am now engaged to a Fräulein Frieda Brandenfeld, a girl from a well-to-do family that settled here a long time after you went away, so that it's very unlikely you'll know her. There will be ample opportunity to tell you more about my fiancée later, but for today let me just say that I am quite happy, and as far as our relationship is concerned, the only change will be that instead of a quite ordinary friend you will now have in me a happy friend. Besides that, you will acquire in my fiancée, who sends you her warm regards and who will soon be writing you herself, a genuine friend of the opposite sex, which is not without importance to a bachelor. I know that there are many reasons why you can't come to pay us a visit, but wouldn't my wedding be just the perfect occasion to put aside everything that might stand in the way? Still, however that may be, do just as seems good to you without regarding any interests but your own."

With this letter in his hand, Georg had been sitting a long time at his desk, his face turned toward the window. He had barely acknowledged, with an absent smile, a greeting waved to him from the street below by a passing acquaintance.

At last he put the letter in his pocket and went out of his room across a small hallway into his father's room, which he had not entered for months. There was, in fact, no particular need for him to enter it, since he saw his father daily at work and they took their midday meal together at a restaurant; in the evening, it was true, each did as he pleased, yet even then, unless Georg—as was usually the case—went out with friends or, more recently, visited his fiancée, they always sat for a while, each with his newspaper, in their common sitting room.

Georg was startled at how dark his father's room was, even on this sunny morning. He had not remembered that it was so overshadowed by the high wall on the other side of the narrow courtyard. His father was sitting by the window in a corner decorated with various mementos of Georg's late mother, reading a newspaper which he held tilted to one side before his eyes in an attempt to compensate for some defect in his vision. On the table stood the remains of his breakfast, little of which seemed to have been consumed.

"Ah, Georg," said his father, rising at once to meet him. His heavy dressing gown swung open as he walked, and its skirts fluttered around him. My father is still a giant of a man, Georg said to himself.

"It's unbearably dark in here," he said aloud.

"Yes, it is dark," answered his father.

"And you've shut the window, too?"

"I prefer it like that."

"Well, it's quite warm outside," said Georg, as if continuing his previous remark, and sat down.

His father cleared away the breakfast dishes and set them on a chest.

"I really only wanted to tell you," Georg went on, following the old man's movements as if transfixed, "that I have just announced the news of my engagement to St. Petersburg." He drew the letter a little way from his pocket and let it drop back again.

"To St. Petersburg?" asked his father.

"To my friend, of course," said Georg, trying to meet his father's eye. In business hours he's quite different, he was thinking, how solidly he sits here and folds his arms over his chest.

"Ah, yes. To your friend," said his father emphatically.

"Well, you know, Father, that I didn't want to tell him about my engagement at first. Out of consideration for him—that was the only reason. You yourself know how difficult a man he is. I said to myself that someone else might tell him about my engagement, although he's such a solitary creature that that was hardly likely, but I wasn't ever going to tell him myself."

"And now you've changed your mind, have you?" asked his father, laying his enormous newspaper on the windowsill and on top of it his eyeglasses, which he covered with one hand.

"Yes, now I've changed my mind. If he's a good friend of mine, I said to myself, then my being happily engaged should make him happy too. And that's why I haven't put off telling him any longer. But before I mailed the letter I wanted to let you know."

"Georg," said his father, stretching his toothless mouth wide, "listen to me! You've come to me about this business, to talk it over and get my advice. No doubt that does you honor. But it's nothing, it's worse than nothing, if you don't tell me the whole truth. I don't want to stir up matters that shouldn't be mentioned here. Since the death of our dear mother certain things have happened that aren't very pretty. Maybe the time will come for mentioning them, and maybe sooner than we think. There are a number of things at the shop that escape my notice, maybe they're not done behind my back—I'm not going to say that they're done behind my back—I'm not strong enough any more, my memory's slipping, I haven't an eye for all those details any longer. In the first place that's in the nature of things, and in the second place the death of our dear little mother hit me harder than it did you. But since we're talking about it, about this letter, I beg you, Georg, don't deceive me. It's a trivial thing, it's hardly worth mentioning, so don't deceive me. Do you really have this friend in St. Petersburg?"

Georg rose in embarrassment. "Never mind my friends. A thousand friends could never replace my father for me. Do you know what I think? You're not taking enough care of yourself. But old age has its own rightful demands. I can't do without you in the business, you know that very well, but if the business is going to undermine your health, I'm ready to close it down tomorrow for good. This won't do. We'll have to make a change in the way you live; a radical change. You sit here in the dark, and in the sitting room you would have plenty of light. You just take a bite of breakfast instead of keeping up your strength properly. You sit by a closed window, and the air would be so good for you. No, Father! I'll get the doctor to come, and we'll follow his orders. We'll change rooms, you can move into the front room and I'll move in here. You won't notice the change, all your things will be moved across the hall with you. But there's time for all that later, go to bed now for a little, you must have some rest. Come, I'll help you to take off your things, you'll see I can do it. Or if you would rather go into the front room at once, you can lie down in my bed for the present. That would actually be the most sensible thing."

Georg stood close beside his father, who had let his head with its shaggy white hair sink to his chest.

"Georg," said his father in a low voice, without moving.

Georg knelt down at once beside his father. In the old man's weary face he saw the abnormally large pupils staring at him fixedly from the corners of the eyes.

"You have no friend in St. Petersburg. You've always been one for pulling people's legs and you haven't hesitated even when it comes to me. How could you have a friend there, of all places! I can't believe it."

"Just think back a bit, Father," said Georg, lifting his father from the chair and slipping off his dressing gown as he stood there, now quite feebly, "soon it'll be three years since my friend came to see us last. I remember you didn't like him very much. At least twice I even told you he wasn't there when he was actually sitting with me in my room. I could quite well understand your dislike of him, my friend does have his peculiarities. But then later you had a good talk with him after all. I was so proud because you listened to him and nodded and asked him questions. If you think back you're bound to remember. He told us the most incredible stories of the Russian Revolution. For instance, the time he was on a business trip to Kiev and ran into a riot, and saw a priest on a balcony who cut a broad cross in blood into the palm of his hand and held the hand up and appealed to the crowd. You've told that very story yourself once or twice since."

Meanwhile Georg had succeeded in lowering his father into the chair again and carefully taking off the knitted drawers he wore over his linen undershorts and his socks. The not particularly clean appearance of his underwear made Georg reproach himself for having been so neglectful. It should certainly have been his duty to see that his father had clean changes of underwear. He had not yet explicitly discussed with his fiancée what arrangements should be made for his father in the future, for they had both silently taken it for granted that he would remain alone in the old apartment. But now he made a quick, firm decision to take him into his own future home. It almost looked, on closer inspection, as if the care he meant to devote to his father there might come too late.

He carried his father over to the bed in his arms. It gave him a dreadful feeling to observe that while he was taking the few steps toward the bed, the old man cradled against his chest was playing with his watch chain. For a moment he could not put him down on the bed, so firmly did he hang on to the watch chain.

But as soon as he was laid in bed, all seemed well. He covered himself up and even drew the blanket higher than usual over his shoulders. He looked up at Georg with a not unfriendly expression.

"You're beginning to remember my friend, aren't you?" asked Georg, giving him an encouraging nod.

"Am I well covered up now?" asked his father, as if he couldn't see whether his feet were properly tucked in or not.

"So you like it in bed, don't you?" said Georg, and tucked the blanket more closely around him.

"Am I well covered up?" the father asked once more, seeming to be peculiarly intent upon the answer.

"Don't worry, you're well covered up."

"No!" cried his father, so that the answer collided with the question, and flinging the blanket back so violently that for a moment it hovered unfolded in the air, he stood upright in bed. With one hand he lightly touched the ceiling to steady himself. "You wanted to cover me up, I know, my little puppy, but I'm far from being covered up yet. And even if this is the last bit of strength I have, it's enough for you, more than enough. Of course I know your friend. He would have been a son after my own heart. That's why you've been betraying him all these years. Why else? Do you think I haven't wept for him? And that's why you've had to lock yourself up in the office—the boss is busy, mustn't be disturbed—just so that you could write your lying little letters to Russia. But fortunately a father doesn't need to be taught how to see through his own son. And now that you thought you'd pinned him down, so far down that you could plant your rear end on him so he couldn't move, then my fine son decides to up and get married!"

Georg looked up at the terrifying image of his father. His friend in St. Petersburg, whom his father suddenly knew so well, seized hold of his imagination as never before. He saw him lost in the vastness of Russia; at the door of his empty, plundered warehouse he saw him. Amid the wreckage of his storage shelves, the slashed remnants of his wares, the falling gas brackets, he barely stood upright. Why did he have to go so far away!

"Pay attention to me!" cried his father, and Georg, almost absent-mindedly, ran toward the bed to take everything in, but froze halfway there.

"Because she lifted up her skirts," his father began to flute, "because she lifted her skirts like this, the revolting creature"— and mimicking her, he lifted his shirt so high that one could see the scar on his thigh from his war wound—"because she lifted her skirts like this and this and this you went after her, and in order to have your way with her undisturbed you have disgraced our mother's memory, betrayed your friend, and stuck your father into bed so that he can't move. But can he move, or can't he?"

And he stood up quite unsupported and kicked his legs about. He shone with insight.

Georg shrank into a corner, as far away from his father as possible. A long time ago he had firmly made up his mind to watch everything with the greatest attention so that he would not be surprised by any indirect attack, a pounce from behind or above. At this moment he recalled this long-forgotten resolve and then forgot it again, like someone drawing a short thread through the eye of a needle.

"But your friend hasn't been betrayed after all!" cried his father, emphasizing the point with stabs of his forefinger. "I've been representing him here on the spot."

"You comedian!" Georg could not resist shouting, realized at once the harm done, and, his eyes bulging in his head, bit his tongue—though too late—until the pain made his knees buckle.

"Yes, of course I've been playing a comedy! A comedy! That's the perfect word for it! What other consolation was left for your poor old widowed father? Tell me—and while you're answering me may you still be my loving son—what else was left to me, in my back room, plagued by a disloyal staff, old to the very marrow of my bones? And my son strutting through the world, closing deals that I had prepared for him, turning somersaults in his glee, and striding away from his father with the composed face of a man of honor! Do you think I didn't love you, I, from whose loins you sprang?"

Now he's going to lean forward, thought Georg; if only he would topple over and smash to pieces! These words went hissing through his brain.

His father leaned forward but did not topple. Since Georg didn't come any closer, as he had expected, he straightened himself up again.

"Stay where you are, then, I don't need you! You think you have the strength to get yourself over here and that you're only hanging back because you want to? Don't be too sure! I am still much the stronger. All by myself I might have had to give in, but your mother has given me her strength, I have established a fine connection with your friend, and I have your customers in my pocket!"

"He has pockets even in his undershirt!" said Georg to himself, and thought that with this observation he could expose him for a fool for all the world to see. He was able to cling to that thought for no more than a moment, for in his distraction he kept on forgetting everything.

"Just try linking arms with your bride and getting in my way! I'll sweep her from your side, you don't know how!"

Georg grimaced in disbelief. His father only nodded in the direction of Georg's corner, affirming the truth of his words.

"How you amused me today, coming in here to ask if you should tell your friend about your engagement. He knows all about it already, you stupid boy, he knows it all! I've been writing to him, for you forgot to take my writing things from me. That's why he hasn't been here for years, he knows everything a hundred times better than you do yourself, with his left hand he crumples up your letters unopened while with his right he holds mine and reads them through!"

In his exhilaration he waved his arm over his head. "He knows everything a thousand times better!" he cried.

"Ten thousand times!" said Georg, to make fun of his father, but in his very mouth the words turned deadly earnest.

"For years I've been waiting for you to come with this question! Do you think I've concerned myself with anything else? Do you think I've been reading my newspapers? Look!" and he threw Georg a page from a newspaper that had somehow found its way into the bed with him. An old newspaper, with a name entirely unknown to Georg.

"How long it's taken you to grow up! Your mother had to die—she couldn't live to see the happy day—your friend is going to pieces in Russia, even three years ago he was yellow enough to be thrown away, and as for me, you can see what condition I'm in. You have eyes in your head for that!"

"So you've been lying in wait for me!" cried Georg.

His father said pityingly, in an offhand manner: "I suppose you wanted to say that earlier. But now it is no longer appropriate."

And in a louder voice: "So now you know there is more in the world than just you. Till now you've known only about yourself! An innocent child, yes, that you were, truly, but still more truly have you been a devilish human being! And therefore take note: I sentence you now to death by drowning!"

Georg felt himself driven from the room, the crash with which his father collapsed onto the bed behind him still rang in his ears as he fled. On the staircase, which he rushed down as if its steps were an inclined plane, he ran into the cleaning woman on her way up to do the morning tidying of the apartment. "Jesus!" she cried, and covered her face with her apron, but he was already gone. Out the front door he bolted, across the roadway, driven toward the water. Already he was clutching at the railing as a starving man clutches for food. He swung himself over, like the accomplished gymnast he had been in his youth, to his parents' pride. With weakening grip he was still holding on when he spied between the railings an approaching bus that would easily cover the sound of his fall, called out in a faint voice, "Dear parents, I have always loved you," and let himself drop.

At that moment an almost endless line of traffic streamed over the bridge. ∾

INTERPRETIVE QUESTIONS
FOR DISCUSSION

Why does Kafka claim in his letter that he is afraid of his father, not that he is angry or resentful toward him?

1. Why does Kafka repeatedly insist that he never for a single moment believes any guilt to be on his father's side, even though he accuses his father of a "total lack of feeling for the suffering and shame you could inflict on me with your words and judgments"? (236, 238, 242–243)

2. Why does Kafka say that he and his father were in their difference "dangerous to each other"? (238)

3. Why does Kafka say that he and his father might have "got on with each other excellently" if only they had not been father and son? (237)

4. Why does Kafka defend his father's actions in the *pavlatche* incident, despite the fact that it caused him "inner harm," instilling the "tormenting fancy" that an authority might take him away for no reason at all? (239–240)

5. Why does Kafka say that his father's aversion to his writing was "welcome," and that he was delighted by this "new confirmation" of his own view of their relationship? (267–268)

6. Why does Kafka describe his writing as "an intentionally long and drawn-out leave-taking" from his father? (268)

7. Why, according to Kafka, has he not been able to make use of the freedom his father has given him to choose a career? (270–271)

8. Why does Kafka believe that he needs the "correction" made by his father's imagined rejoinder for his letter to approximate the truth? Why does he think that this truth might make their living and their dying easier? (283)

9. Why does Kafka include in his father's imaginary rejoinder the claim that he is not sincere in absolving his father of all guilt? Does Kafka believe any of the accusations he imagines his father making? (282)

10. Why does Kafka imagine his father accusing him of "preying on me even with this letter itself"? (283)

11. Does Kafka consciously use his father's own "methods"—abuse, irony, and self-pity—to wound him? Does Kafka write the letter to unburden himself, or does he believe his father can learn something?

12. Does his father's "method of upbringing" turn Kafka into a writer?

Suggested textual analyses

Pages 235–238: beginning, "You asked me recently," and ending, "that I succumbed to that effect."

Pages 281–283: from "If you look at the reasons I offer," to the end of the selection.

Why does the "success" of Kafka's letter depend on its ability to make his attempts to marry comprehensible to his father?

1. Why did Kafka's father make it all but impossible for his son to marry?

2. Why does Kafka believe that Elli's marriage altered her essential character—changing her from an abhorrent child to a "cheerful, carefree, brave, generous, unselfish, and hopeful" woman? (258)

3. Why, according to Kafka, are all of the positive forces "at [his] disposal" and the negative forces of his upbringing concentrated in his attempts to marry? (272)

4. Why does Kafka think that his attempts at marriage have had more importance for him than anything that has happened to his father in his whole life? (272–273)

5. Why does Kafka think that marrying and founding a family is "the utmost a human being can succeed in doing at all"? (273)

6. Why does his father's candid advice on sexual matters disturb Kafka as much at age thirty-six as at age sixteen? Why does Kafka cite both cases as evidence for his and his father's mutual "guiltlessness"? (274–276)

7. Why does Kafka compare himself to a prisoner with inconsistent desires—to both escape his prison and rebuild it "as a pleasure dome for himself"? (278)

8. Why can't Kafka benefit from his father's example in marriage, even though he admits it is a good one? (279)

9. Why does Kafka imagine his father stretched across a map of the world, and himself capable of living only in those regions not covered by his father or within his reach? (279)

10. Why does Kafka cite as one of his reasons for not marrying the fact that he would find a "mute, glum, dry, doomed son" such as himself "unbearable"? (279)

11. Why can Kafka find the independence he craves only in writing? Why is marriage a threat to this independence? (280)

12. Why does Kafka think that by writing his letter he will achieve "a kind of peace" with his father? (236)

Suggested textual analyses

Pages 272–273: beginning, "But I showed no foresight," and ending, "and one can warm oneself a little."

Pages 279–281: beginning, "But we being what we are," and ending, "And now marry without going mad!"

Why does Georg carry out the death sentence pronounced upon him by his father in "The Judgment"?

1. Why does Georg find himself in a quandary about whether or not to be honest with his friend who has left the country and "gone badly astray"? (286) Why does he need the prodding of his fiancée in order to tell the truth about his engagement?

2. Why are we told that Georg prospered in business after his mother's death?

3. Why does Georg, having written to his friend, want to let his father know of the letter before mailing it? Why does the father say that for years he has been waiting for Georg to ask whether he should tell his friend about his engagement?

4. Why does Georg's weakened father again become vigorous—strong and agile and shining "with insight"—when opposing Georg? (294)

5. Why does Georg suddenly feel empathy and compassion for his friend's situation in Russia after his father claims to have "wept for him"? (293)

6. Why does the father at first question the existence of Georg's friend in St. Petersburg and then claim to be his representative? Why does he compete with Georg over the friendship as well as over his bride-to-be?

7. Why does Georg's father denigrate and mimic his son's relations with his fiancée? Why does he accuse Georg of disgracing his mother, betraying his friend, and sticking his "father into bed so that he can't move"? (294)

8. Why does Georg react to his father's suggestion that he loves him by wishing his father would "topple over and smash to pieces"? (295)

9. Why does Georg's father sentence him to death by drowning when Georg apparently has become successful in business and in love?

10. Why does Georg want a bus to cover the sound of his fall? Why does Georg say, "Dear parents, I have always loved you," before he lets himself drop? (297)

Suggested textual analyses

Pages 287–289: beginning, "But Georg's friend had no inkling," and ending, "in their common sitting room."

Pages 296–297: from "For years I've been waiting," to the end of the story.

FOR FURTHER REFLECTION

1. What kind of father did Kafka need?

2. Can the situation that existed between Kafka and his father be considered "blameless"? Are both parties at fault, or must the father shoulder the blame for their estrangement?

3. Why did Kafka's father fail to rear the kind of son he wanted?

4. Must parents to some extent be tyrants—authorities "whose rights are based on their person and not on reason"?

5. Is it inevitable that children will seek out places on the map not occupied by their parents?

6. Are conflicts such as those between Kafka and his father inevitable when parents grow up in a different socioeconomic environment from their children?

7. Does Kafka overestimate the importance of marriage as a means of breaking away from one's parents' "orbit of influence"?

8. Is there less conflict among parents and children in families where religious feeling is strong?

POETRY

William Butler Yeats

Derek Walcott

Randall Jarrell

Sharon Olds

WILLIAM BUTLER YEATS (1865–1939) had one of
the longest and most productive careers in the
history of letters. In addition to writing fourteen
volumes of poetry, he wrote and produced nineteen
plays, and was the author of twenty-three books
of prose, including both fiction and nonfiction.
From 1922 to 1928, Yeats served as a senator of
the Irish Free State. He was awarded the Nobel
Prize for literature in 1923. T. S. Eliot described
Yeats as the greatest poet of his time—"certainly
the greatest in this language, and so far as
I am able to judge, in any language."

❧

DEREK WALCOTT (1930–   ) was born on the
island of St. Lucia, studied at the University of the
West Indies, and has lived extensively in Great
Britain and the United States. His first major volume of poetry, *In a Green Night,* was published in
1962. In 1992, Walcott won the Nobel Prize for
literature; he was the first West Indian writer to
receive this honor.

RANDALL JARRELL (1914–1965) was a poet, novelist, critic, and teacher. He was educated at Vanderbilt University and taught at a number of colleges and universities throughout the United States. Jarrell received several prestigious awards in his lifetime, including a Guggenheim Fellowship in 1946 and the National Book Award for poetry in 1961. He also served as chancellor of the Academy of American Poets and was the poetry consultant at the Library of Congress from 1956 to 1958. Jarrell wrote for both children and adults.

∾

SHARON OLDS (1942–   ) was born in San Francisco and educated at Stanford and Columbia Universities. She has been awarded both a National Endowment for the Arts grant and a Guggenheim Fellowship. *The Dead and the Living,* from which "Exclusive" is taken, was the 1983 Lamont Poetry Selection of the Academy of American Poets.

Among School Children

1

I WALK through the long schoolroom questioning;
A kind old nun in a white hood replies;
The children learn to cipher and to sing,
To study reading-books and history,
To cut and sew, be neat in everything
In the best modern way—the children's eyes
In momentary wonder stare upon
A sixty-year-old smiling public man.

2

I dream of a Ledaean body,[1] bent
Above a sinking fire, a tale that she
Told of a harsh reproof, or trivial event
That changed some childish day to tragedy—
Told, and it seemed that our two natures blent
Into a sphere from youthful sympathy,
Or else, to alter Plato's parable,[2]
Into the yolk and white of the one shell.

---

1. [*Ledaean body:* In Greek legend, Leda was the mother of Helen of Troy by Zeus, who appeared to Leda in the form of a swan. The "Ledaean body" Yeats has in mind is Maud Gonne, the unrequited love of his life.]

2. [*Plato's parable:* In Plato's *Symposium*, a story is told of how human beings were originally joined together in pairs, forming two-faced, four-legged, four-armed spherical creatures that the gods later divided. According to the legend, lovers are those split halves longing to be reunited.]

3

And thinking of that fit of grief or rage
I look upon one child or t'other there
And wonder if she stood so at that age— *child*
For even daughters of the swan can share
Something of every paddler's heritage—
And had that colour upon cheek or hair,
And thereupon my heart is driven wild:
She stands before me as a living child.

4

Her present image floats into the mind—
Did Quattrocento[3] finger fashion it
Hollow of cheek as though it drank the wind
And took a mess of shadows for its meat?
And I though never of Ledaean kind
Had pretty plumage once—enough of that, *Passage of time*
Better to smile on all that smile, and show
There is a comfortable kind of old scarecrow.

5

What youthful mother, a shape upon her lap
Honey of generation[4] had betrayed,
And that must sleep, shriek, struggle to escape
As recollection or the drug decide,
Would think her son, did she but see that shape
With sixty or more winters on its head,
A compensation for the pang of his birth,
Or the uncertainty of his setting forth?

---

3. [*Quattrocento*: fifteenth century.]

4. [*Honey of generation*: "the 'drug' that destroys the 'recollection' of pre-natal freedom" (from a note to the poem by Yeats).]

6

Plato thought nature but a spume that plays
Upon a ghostly paradigm of things;
Soldier Aristotle played the taws⁵
Upon the bottom of a king of kings;
World-famous golden-thighed Pythagoras
Fingered upon a fiddle-stick or strings
What a star sang and careless Muses heard:
Old clothes upon old sticks to scare a bird.

7

Both nuns and mothers worship images,
But those the candles light are not as those
That animate a mother's reveries,
But keep a marble or a bronze repose.
And yet they too break hearts—O Presences
That passion, piety or affection knows,
And that all heavenly glory symbolise—
O self-born mockers of man's enterprise;

8

Labour is blossoming or dancing where
The body is not bruised to pleasure soul,
Nor beauty born out of its own despair,
Nor blear-eyed wisdom out of midnight oil.
O chestnut-tree, great-rooted blossomer,
Are you the leaf, the blossom or the bole?
O body swayed to music, O brightening glance,
How can we know the dancer from the dance?

William Butler Yeats

---

5. [*played the taws*: whipped with leather straps.]

5

A Prayer for My Daughter

ONCE MORE the storm is howling, and half hid
Under this cradle-hood and coverlid
My child sleeps on. There is no obstacle
But Gregory's wood and one bare hill
Whereby the haystack- and roof-levelling wind,
Bred on the Atlantic, can be stayed;
And for an hour I have walked and prayed
Because of the great gloom that is in my mind.

I have walked and prayed for this young child an hour
And heard the sea-wind scream upon the tower,
And under the arches of the bridge, and scream
In the elms above the flooded stream;
Imagining in excited reverie
That the future years had come,
Dancing to a frenzied drum,
Out of the murderous innocence of the sea.

future
ominous

May she be granted beauty and yet not
Beauty to make a stranger's eye distraught,
Or hers before a looking-glass, for such,
Being made beautiful overmuch,
Consider beauty a sufficient end,
Lose natural kindness and maybe
The heart-revealing intimacy
That chooses right, and never find a friend.

Helen being chosen found life flat and dull
And later had much trouble from a fool,
While that great Queen, that rose out of the spray,
Being fatherless could have her way
Yet chose a bandy-leggèd smith for man.
It's certain that fine women eat
A crazy salad with their meat
Whereby the Horn of Plenty is undone.

In courtesy I'd have her chiefly learned;
Hearts are not had as a gift but hearts are earned
By those that are not entirely beautiful;
Yet many, that have played the fool
For beauty's very self, has charm made wise,
And many a poor man that has roved,
Loved and thought himself beloved,
From a glad kindness cannot take his eyes.

May she become a flourishing hidden tree
That all her thoughts may like the linnet be,
And have no business but dispensing round
Their magnanimities of sound,
Nor but in merriment begin a chase,
Nor but in merriment a quarrel.
O may she live like some green laurel
Rooted in one dear perpetual place.

My mind, because the minds that I have loved,
The sort of beauty that I have approved,
Prosper but little, has dried up of late,
Yet knows that to be choked with hate
May well be of all evil chances chief.
If there's no hatred in a mind
Assault and battery of the wind
Can never tear the linnet from the leaf.

An intellectual hatred is the worst,
So let her think opinions are accursed.
Have I not seen the loveliest woman born
Out of the mouth of Plenty's horn,
Because of her opinionated mind
Barter that horn and every good
By quiet natures understood
For an old bellows full of angry wind?

Considering that, all hatred driven hence,
The soul recovers radical innocence
And learns at last that it is self-delighting,
Self-appeasing, self-affrighting,
And that its own sweet will is Heaven's will;
She can, though every face should scowl
And every windy quarter howl
Or every bellows burst, be happy still.

And may her bridegroom bring her to a house
Where all's accustomed, ceremonious;
For arrogance and hatred are the wares
Peddled in the thoroughfares.
How but in custom and in ceremony
Are innocence and beauty born?
Ceremony's a name for the rich horn,
And custom for the spreading laurel tree.

William Butler Yeats

A Letter from Brooklyn

AN OLD LADY writes me in a spidery style,
Each character trembling, and I see a veined hand
Pellucid as paper, travelling on a skein
Of such frail thoughts its thread is often broken;
Or else the filament from which a phrase is hung
Dims to my sense, but caught, it shines like steel,
As touch a line, and the whole web will feel.
She describes my father, yet I forget her face
More easily than my father's yearly dying;
Of her I remember small, buttoned boots and the place
She kept in our wooden church on those Sundays
Whenever her strength allowed;
Grey haired, thin voiced, perpetually bowed.

"I am Mable Rawlins," she writes, "and know both your parents;"
He is dead, Miss Rawlins, but God bless your tense:
"Your father was a dutiful, honest,
Faithful and useful person."
For such plain praise what fame is recompense?
"A horn-painter, he painted delicately on horn,
He used to sit around the table and paint pictures."
The peace of God needs nothing to adorn
It, nor glory nor ambition.
"He is twenty-eight years buried," she writes, "he was called home,
And is, I am sure, doing greater work."

The strength of one frail hand in a dim room
Somewhere in Brooklyn, patient and assured,
Restores my sacred duty to the Word.
"Home, home," she can write, with such short time to live,
Alone as she spins the blessings of her years;
Not withered of beauty if she can bring such tears,
Nor withdrawn from the world that breaks its lovers so;
Heaven is to her the place where painters go,
All who bring beauty on frail shell or horn,

There was all made, thence their lux-mundi drawn,
Drawn, drawn, till the thread is resilient steel,
Lost though it seems in darkening periods,
And there they return to do work that is God's.

So this old lady writes, and again I believe,
I believe it all, and for no man's death I grieve.

Derek Walcott

The Lost Children

Two little girls, one fair, one dark,
One alive, one dead, are running hand in hand
Through a sunny house. The two are dressed
In red and white gingham, with puffed sleeves and sashes.
They run away from me . . . But I am happy;
When I wake I feel no sadness, only delight.
I've seen them again, and I am comforted
That, somewhere, they still are.

It is strange
To carry inside you someone else's body;
To know it before it's born;
To see at last that it's a boy or girl, and perfect;
To bathe it and dress it; to watch it
Nurse at your breast, till you almost know it
Better than you know yourself—better than it knows itself.
You own it as you made it.
You are the authority upon it.

But as the child learns
To take care of herself, you know her less.
Her accidents, adventures are her own,
You lose track of them. Still, you know more
About her than anyone *except* her.

Little by little the child in her dies.
You say, "I have lost a child, but gained a friend."
You feel yourself gradually discarded.
She argues with you or ignores you
Or is kind to you. She who begged to follow you
Anywhere, just so long as it was you,
Finds follow the leader no more fun.
She makes few demands; you are grateful for the few.

The young person who writes once a week
Is the authority upon herself.
She sits in my living room and shows her husband
My albums of her as a child. He enjoys them
And makes fun of them. I look too
And I realize the girl in the matching blue
Mother-and-daughter dress, the fair one carrying
The tin lunch box with the half-pint thermos bottle
Or training her pet duck to go down the slide
Is lost just as the dark one, who is dead, is lost.
But the world in which the two wear their flared coats
And the hats that match, exists so uncannily
That, after I've seen its pictures for an hour,
I believe in it: the bandage coming loose
One has in the picture of the other's birthday,
The castles they are building, at the beach for asthma.
I look at them and all the old sure knowledge
Floods over me, when I put the album down
I keep saying inside: "I *did* know those children.
I braided those braids. I was driving the car
The day that she stepped in the can of grease
We were taking to the butcher for our ration points.
I *know* those children. I know all about them.
Where are they?"

I stare at her and try to see some sign
Of the child she was. I can't believe there isn't any.
I tell her foolishly, pointing at the picture,
That I keep wondering where she is.
She tells me, "Here I am."
                              Yes, and the other
Isn't dead, but has everlasting life . . .

The girl from next door, the borrowed child,
Said to me the other day, "You like children so much,
Don't you want to have some of your own?"
I couldn't believe that she could say it.
I thought: "Surely you can look at me and see them."

When I see them in my dreams I feel such joy.
If I could dream of them every night!

When I think of my dream of the little girls
It's as if we were playing hide-and-seek.
The dark one
Looks at me longingly, and disappears;
The fair one stays in sight, just out of reach
No matter where I reach. I am tired
As a mother who's played all day, some rainy day.
I don't want to play it any more, I don't want to,
But the child keeps on playing, so I play.

Randall Jarrell

Exclusive
(for my daughter)

I LIE on the beach, watching you
as you lie on the beach, memorizing you
against the time when you will not be with me:
your empurpled lips, swollen in the sun
and smooth as the inner lips of a shell;
your biscuit-gold skin, glazed and
faintly pitted, like the surface of a biscuit;
the serious knotted twine of your hair.
I have loved you instead of anyone else,
loved you as a way of loving no one else,
every separate grain of your body
building the god, as I built you within me,
a sealed world. What if from your lips
I had learned the love of other lips,
from your starred, gummed lashes the love of
other lashes, from your shut, quivering
eyes the love of other eyes,
from your body the bodies,
from your life the lives?
Today I see it is there to be learned from you:
to love what I do not own.

Sharon Olds

Interpretive Questions
for Discussion

In "Among School Children," why does being in a classroom of children prompt the poet to ask, "How can we know the dancer from the dance"?

1. Why does the poet feel such deep sympathy for the woman he is remembering when he recalls her tale of childhood "tragedy"?

2. Why is the poet "driven wild" by imagining his beloved as an ordinary child who shared "something of every paddler's heritage"?

3. Why does the poet contrast the living image of his beloved as a child—inspired by the real children around him—with the "Quattrocento" image of her as she is now?

4. Why does the poet recall his own "pretty plumage"? Why does he dismiss this thought, preferring instead to smile and be "a comfortable kind of old scarecrow"?

5. Why does the poet think of a child as having been "betrayed" by the "honey of generation"? Why does he doubt that if a young mother could foresee what her child would become, she would consider him a "compensation for the pang of his birth,/Or the uncertainty of his setting forth"?

6. Why does the poet think of the great philosophers of the past as scarecrows like himself—"old clothes upon old sticks to scare a bird"? Why at this moment do they seem less important than the ordinary children he sees around him?

7. Why does the poet insist that "both nuns and mothers worship images," even though for nuns these are statues and for mothers living children? Why does he remark that both kinds of images "break hearts"?

8. Why does the poet describe the images that are the focus of human "passion, piety or affection" as "Presences"? Why are they both symbols of "all heavenly glory" and "self-born mockers of man's enterprise"?

9. Why does the poet think of the school children as "labour" that is "blossoming or dancing" where there is no struggle or drudgery? Why does the poet ask whether a chestnut tree is leaf, blossom, or bole?

10. Does being among school children ultimately reaffirm the poet's belief in the value of life?

4 or 5

In "A Prayer for My Daughter," why doesn't the poet want his daughter to be exceptional?

1. Why does the poet have a "great gloom" in his mind about the future of his daughter, even though she is still only an infant? Why does he feel he needs to pray for his daughter, rather than plan well for her upbringing?

2. Why does the poet regard the future as a threat to his daughter? Why does he imagine the threat coming from "the murderous innocence of the sea"?

3. Why does the poet think his daughter could not withstand the danger that great beauty represents to her character?   5+ 3-4

4. Why does the poet want his daughter to learn courtesy above all else? Why does he think courtesy is the way that "hearts are earned"?

5+ 5

5. Why does the poet think that the best thing for his daughter would be for her to live rooted in one place like a tree, yet with thoughts that come and go freely like a playful bird?

6. Why does the poet think that intellectual hatred is the worst of all evils? *Stanza 8*

7. Does the poet believe he can teach his daughter "radical innocence"? Is "radical innocence" a state of profound wisdom, or a lack of spiritual and mental development? *recovers*

8. Why does the poet, who chiefly wants his daughter to learn courtesy, also wish that she behave as if her "own sweet will is Heaven's will"?

9. Why does the poet think that innocence and beauty can be "born" only in custom and ceremony?

10. Is the poet more concerned that his daughter know how to get along with people, or that she be self-sufficient and independent?

In "A Letter from Brooklyn," why does reading the old woman's letter about his father enable the poet to regain his belief and overcome his grief?

1. Why does the poet insist that the old woman's prose "shines like steel," despite its imperfections? *like a spider's web*

2. Why is it a person whose words are neither eloquent nor profound who restores to the poet his "sacred duty to the Word"?

3. Does the poet share Miss Rawlins' view of heaven? Are we meant to think that he believes in the same way that she believes?

4. Why does the poet say he believes "again"? Why does he say he believes "it all"?

5. Why does the poet overcome his grief, not only for his father's death, but for anyone's?

6. Is it a renewed faith in art that enables the poet to accept death?

Why does the woman in "The Lost Children" consider her living daughter just as "lost" as the daughter who died?

1. Why is the woman happy when she dreams of her two little girls, even though they run away from her? Why does she feel no sadness when she wakes, only delight?

2. Why does the woman say that "you own" your child "as you made it"? Are we meant to think that this is an unhealthy attitude?

3. Why does the woman think that as her daughter grows up "the child in her dies"?

4. What is "the old sure knowledge" that "floods over" the woman as she looks through the picture album?

5. Are we meant to think that the death of one of the woman's daughters has made it impossible for her to love the other?

6. Why is the woman unable to take joy in seeing her daughter grow up and be happy?

7. Why is the woman unable to see in her adult daughter any sign of the child the daughter once was? Why does she tell her daughter, as they are looking at childhood pictures, that she wonders where she is?

8. When the daughter says, "Here I am," why does the mother think, "Yes, and the other / Isn't dead, but has everlasting life . . ."?

9. Why does the woman think that the girl from next door should be able to see her children by looking at her?

10. Why is the woman tired of playing her dream game of hide-and-seek if it gives her such joy? Why does she keep on playing the game if she is tired of it?

Why is the poet in "Exclusive" able to learn from her daughter how to love what she does not own?

1. Why does the poet deal with the prospective loss of her daughter by "memorizing" her?

2. Why does the poet say she has loved her daughter "as a way of loving no one else"?

3. Why does the poet address her words to her daughter, but not actually speak to her?

4. Why does the poet think of "every separate grain" of her daughter's body as "building the god"?

5. Why does the poet wonder what might have been if she had learned from her daughter's life to love other lives?

6. Why, according to the poem, has the poet's love for her daughter been exclusive? Why did the poet choose to love what she owned or thought herself to own?

7. Is the poet letting go of her daughter, or does she fail to see her daughter as an individual even at the end of the poem?

8. Does the poet see herself as having sacrificed her own life for her daughter?

FOR FURTHER REFLECTION

1. Do most parents worship images of their children?

2. Do mothers and fathers love differently?

3. Do you think courtesy, custom, and ceremony can help a person survive in a chaotic world?

4. Is life better as a child or as an adult?

5. Is there any way to prepare for letting go of your children as they become adults? Can this transition be made to go smoothly for both parent and child?

6. Have you ever thought of yourself as owning your children?

7. How much control do parents have over whether their children live joyfully or sorrowfully?

Questions for

PERSUASION

Jane Austen

JANE AUSTEN (1775–1817) is one of the great masters of the English novel. Her works are renowned for their penetrating satire, innovative narrative style, and moral vision. Not many details are known of Austen's life, but the inscription above her tomb in Winchester Cathedral provides these particulars: "youngest daughter of the late Rev. George Austen, formerly Rector of Steventon in this County, she departed this Life on the 18th of July 1817, aged 41, after a long illness supported with the patience and the hopes of a Christian. The benevolence of her heart, the sweetness of her temper, and the extraordinary endowments of her mind obtained the regard of all who knew her, and the warmest love of her intimate connections." No mention is made of Austen's novels, because her name never appeared on the title page of the four books published during her lifetime—*Sense and Sensibility, Pride and Prejudice, Mansfield Park,* and *Emma.* Austen's two other completed novels, *Northanger Abbey* and *Persuasion,* were published posthumously in 1818.

NOTE: All page references are from the Bantam Classic edition of *Persuasion* (first printing 1984).

INTERPRETIVE QUESTIONS
FOR DISCUSSION

Why does Anne recover her bloom of beauty when she leaves her father's house?

1. Why are Anne's friends and relations at Uppercross oblivious to what a trial it is for her to leave Kellynch? Why must Anne "submit" to the lesson of "knowing our own nothingness beyond our own circle"? (35)

2. Why do both Uppercross households value Anne's good sense and tact, whereas Sir Walter and Elizabeth regard her as "nobody"? (3, 37–39) Why do Mary's children obey Anne, but not their own mother? (31, 49)

3. Why does Anne submit "fully . . . in silent, deep mortification" when she is told that Captain Wentworth considers her "altered beyond his knowledge"? Why, after dwelling on these words, is Anne able to use them to make herself more composed, and consequently happier? (52)

4. Why does Anne become so agitated and confused by the incident in which Captain Wentworth removes little Walter from her back? Why does she feel so deeply ashamed of herself for having reacted so strongly? (69–70)

5. Why does Anne feel well repaid for making an effort to converse with Captain Benwick? (88)

6. Why is Anne's pain at the loss of Captain Wentworth softened rather than rekindled during her two-month stay at Uppercross? (106)

7. Why does the visit to Uppercross cause a mental as well as a physical change in Anne? Why did the subjects that had filled her heart upon leaving Kellynch become of secondary interest to her? (107)

8. Why does Anne value a warm, open nature more than any other and feel mortified at the "heartless elegance" of her sister and father? (141, 201)

9. Why does Anne, who has no great value for rank and connections, end up wishing that her father and sister had more pride? (129–130) Why does Anne conclude that she has more pride than her family, Mr. Elliot, and Lady Russell? (131–132)

10. In saying that Anne "had been too dependant on time alone" to get over her romance with Captain Wentworth, is the author suggesting that Anne would have gotten over her attachment if she had traveled more widely or been more valued by her family? (23–24) What does the author mean when she says that Anne "learned romance as she grew older"? (25)

Suggested textual analyses

Pages 68–70 (from Chapter 9): beginning, "One morning, very soon after the dinner at the Musgroves," and ending, "a long application of solitude and reflection to recover her."

Pages 106–109 (from Chapter 13): beginning, "If Louisa recovered," and ending, "she had no sigh of that description to heave."

Why is Lady Russell unable to guide Anne toward achieving happiness, despite her good sense and love for Anne?

1. Why doesn't Anne ever speak to Lady Russell about her attachment to Captain Wentworth and her feelings eight years later? Why does Anne blame neither herself nor Lady Russell for acting as they did, even though, in similar circumstances, Anne would give a young person very different advice? (24; cf. 218)

2. Why does Lady Russell think that Anne would have been "throwing away" herself if she had married Captain Wentworth, even though he had "a great deal of intelligence, spirit and brilliancy"? (21–22)

3. Why do Captain Wentworth's sanguine temper and fearlessness of mind bewitch Anne but horrify Lady Russell? Why are we told that when Captain Wentworth first knew Anne, he had been lucky in his profession, "but spending freely, what had come freely, had realized nothing"? (22)

4. Why are we told that Lady Russell, along with Anne, tended to believe that Charles Musgrove might have improved in character, usefulness, rationality, and elegance had he married more wisely? (36)

5. Why do Lady Russell and Captain Wentworth "not like each other"? (82)

6. Why does Lady Russell revel "in angry pleasure, in pleased contempt, that the man who at twenty-three had seemed to understand somewhat of the value of an Anne Elliot, should, eight years afterwards, be charmed by a Louisa Musgrove"? (108)

7. Why doesn't Lady Russell see through Mr. Elliot's too agreeable nature as Anne does? (128) Why is Lady Russell more willing than Anne to forgive Mr. Elliot's past bad habits and conduct? (141–142)

8. Why does Anne believe that, despite her better judgment and past experience, she might have been persuaded by Lady Russell to marry Mr. Elliot? (187)

9. After reaching an understanding with Captain Wentworth, why does Anne retreat to the privacy of her room for an "interval of meditation, serious and grateful"? Why must Anne grow "steadfast and fearless" in the thankfulness of her happiness? (219)

10. Why does the author include "one independent fortune" with the advantages of maturity and conscience that lead to the happy union of Anne and Captain Wentworth? (221)

Suggested textual analysis
Pages 8–13 and 21–26 (Chapters 2 and 4)

Why does Captain Wentworth claim that he was never inconstant to Anne?

1. Why does Captain Wentworth still resent Anne eight years after their broken engagement, and mistake her commitment to conscience and duty toward Lady Russell as "feebleness of character"? (53)

2. Why doesn't Captain Wentworth believe that Anne gave him up because she thought it would be better for him not to be bound to their engagement? (23)

3. Why does Anne find Captain Wentworth's cold politeness and ceremonious grace at Uppercross "worse than any thing"? (63)

4. Why is there no love among Louisa, Henrietta, and Captain Wentworth, only "a little fever of admiration"? (71) Why is the sensitive and principled Captain Wentworth unaware of the pain he is causing Henrietta, Louisa, and Charles Hayter, and that his actions might be impeaching his own honor? (67, 71)

5. Why does Captain Wentworth mistake Louisa Musgrove's headstrong willfulness for conviction and strength of mind—qualities that Anne has possessed all along? (103)

6. Why is the story told so that by giving Louisa "the idea of merit in maintaining her own way," Captain Wentworth threatens her life and the happiness of the large family who loves her? (82; cf. 106)

7. Why does Captain Wentworth recognize in Benwick, but not in Anne, a disposition "of the sort which must suffer heavily, uniting very strong feelings with quiet, serious, and retiring manners, and a decided taste for reading, and sedentary pursuits"? (85)

8. Why does the rekindling of Captain Wentworth's love for Anne begin when he notices Mr. Elliot's admiration of her?

9. Why can't Anne and Captain Wentworth be united until Anne—the consummate listener—is listened to and heard by Captain Wentworth? Why do Anne's words, which carry "no weight" with her family, pierce the soul of Captain Wentworth? (196, 211; cf. 3)

10. Why does it turn out that Captain Wentworth—and not Lady Russell—was his own worst enemy? (221)

Suggested textual analysis
Pages 204–221 (Chapter 23)

FOR FURTHER REFLECTION

1. Should parents try to persuade their children about decisions as important as whom—or whom not—to marry?

2. Do women love longer than men when existence or hope is gone?

3. Could Anne's story still be told today, when women are more mobile and worldly, and social intercourse is less formal and restricted?

4. Is it difficult to recognize the quality of a gentle but resolute spirit like Anne's, or was she simply surrounded by a lot of dull and selfish people?

5. Do you agree that life experience cannot develop a person's ability to discern character—that this requires "a natural penetration"?

6. Do spouses become parents of sorts to their mates, and form characters either for ill or for good?

Questions for

BILLIARDS AT
HALF-PAST NINE

Heinrich Böll

HEINRICH BÖLL (1917–1985) was born
in Cologne and grew up in a liberal,
Catholic, pacifist family. Drafted into the
Wehrmacht in 1938, he served on the
Russian and French fronts and was wounded
four times before ending up in an American
prison camp in 1945. Böll served as the
president of the International Association of
Poets, Playwrights, Editors, Essayists, and
Novelists (PEN) for several years. In 1972,
he won the Nobel Prize for literature.

NOTE: All page references are from the Penguin
Twentieth-Century Classics edition of *Billiards at Half-past
Nine* (first printing 1994).

INTERPRETIVE QUESTIONS
FOR DISCUSSION

Why does Robert play billiards in the Prince Heinrich Hotel every morning from half-past nine to eleven?

1. Why does Robert play a solitary version of the game he once played with Schrella in Holland? (166)

2. Why does Robert regard the time he spends playing billiards as inviolable, except by his immediate family or Schrella?

3. Why does Leonore perceive Robert's office as a place of "perfect order" with a "flawlessly dressed and unfailingly polite employer who gave you the creeps"? Why can she sense contempt behind Robert's politeness? (2–3)

4. Why does Robert adhere to a rigorous yet arbitrary schedule, making it a rule never to spend more than an hour a day in the office? Why is even his heavy drinking carefully regulated? (5–6)

5. Why does Robert give up playing billiards according to the rules? Why does he instead become fascinated with "the swirl of lines" in which there are "no abiding forms, nothing lasting, all fleeting, force expended in a mere rolling of spheres"? (31)

6. Why doesn't Robert realize at first that he has been telling stories to Hugo as he shoots billiards? (32)

7. Why does the author have the Prince Heinrich Hotel's policy of discretion both ensure Robert his privacy and hide the activities of adulterers, suicides, and frauds? (17)

8. Why does time cease "to be a dimension making things measurable" during Robert and Hugo's conversations in the billiard room? (47) Why, once Schrella arrives, does the billiard game become resituated in the present moment? (267–268)

9. Why does Robert suggest that he and Schrella quit playing billiards? Why is the game no longer necessary? (268)

10. In refusing to allow anyone to disturb his billiard game, is Robert taking a moral stand against the injustices of German society, or withdrawing from the world and from responsibility?

Suggested textual analyses
Pages 1–8 (from Chapter 1): from the beginning of the chapter to "We're not in the business here of collecting confessions, are we?"

Pages 31–43 (from Chapter 3): from the beginning of the chapter to "And I said, 'That's right, I'm a beggar.' "

Why does Robert blow up the abbey that his father built?

1. Why does Robert become an architect like his father, but, unlike him, one who has "never built a house . . . an architect of the writing desk"? (149) Why does Robert prefer destruction and rebuilding to restoration? (202)

2. Why does Robert's father think him "quite capable of committing murder"? (15)

3. Why does Robert think of the destroyed St. Anthony's Abbey as "a monument of dust and rubble for those who had not been historical monuments and whom no one had thought to spare"? (156)

4. Why does old Faehmel describe Robert as always being "clever and cool and never ironic," whereas Otto, whom he had loved so much, "had a heart"? (91, 92)

5. Why does Robert refuse to explain to the American officer why he blew up the abbey? Why does he think that "even if he had said why, it wouldn't have been why any more"? (156)

6. Why does Robert tell the American officer that he destroyed the abbey "perhaps . . . for the fun of it," and suggest that part of his motivation was his "pure delight" in mathematics and his interest in "knowing which forces are required to undo the laws of statics"? (159)

7. Why doesn't Robert want his memories of St. Anthony's to "disintegrate" into feelings of bliss or grief? Why is Robert's heart "not involved" when he visits the abbey with his family, his memories remaining "formula," not transposed into feelings? (225, 229)

8. Why is Robert "not reconciled either to [him]self or to the spirit of reconciliation" espoused by the abbot who is rebuilding St. Anthony's? Why does the unrepentant Robert believe that hatred destroyed the abbot's home, not blind passion? (228)

9. Why do both Robert's father and son guess that Robert destroyed the abbey, but never say anything about it? Why do they accept without anger or wonder that Robert destroyed the abbey so deeply connected to the Faehmel family?

10. Why does the author have all three generations of Faehmels— father, son, and grandson—refuse to help in the reconstruction of St. Anthony's Abbey? (228–229)

Suggested textual analyses

Pages 154–160 (from Chapter 6): beginning, "The American officer," and ending, *"Firm in compassion the eternal heart."*

Pages 225–230 (from Chapter 10): from the beginning of the chapter to "the prey that would escape us: St. Severin's."

Are we meant to think that old Faehmel was complicit in promoting the evil that led to Germany's involvement in World War II?

1. Why does old Faehmel call his pursuit of success a "dance," a "game," and a "play"? (71, 79, 97–98, 103) Why does he claim that he has never figured out his motives, but speculate that the wish to propagate a myth about himself might have been his goal all along? (67, 69, 76; cf. 140–141)

2. Why does old Faehmel say that there was "mockery and derision" and "even malice" in his youthful laughter as he contemplated his future? (69) Why, despite his irony and cynicism, did old Faehmel love Kilb's daughter, Johanna, and the young abbot of St. Anthony's? (109)

3. Why does old Faehmel regret that he didn't stand up and agree with Johanna when she denounced "that fool of a Kaiser" and the militarism of World War I? (81–83, 90–91)

4. Are we meant to see old Faehmel's decision to have Johanna committed to an asylum as necessary and inevitable, or as an example of moral cowardice?

5. Why does old Faehmel tell Leonore that she must spit on the monument they erect to him? (91, 116) Why does Johanna tell old Faehmel that he must make sure no monument is ever built? (251)

6. Why does Johanna say that her husband is a "child," with "no idea how bad the world is," and "a quiet man, no blemishes on his pure heart"? (123) Why does Robert say that his father is one of the few people to whom he would entrust his life? (166)

7. Why does old Faehmel describe his pursuit of the St. Anthony's commission in terms that echo Hitler's assault on Europe: "[T]he future was mine for the taking, like a country waiting to be conquered. . . . All I had to do was march in. . . . I was already deep inside the country and half in possession of it with the enemy still asleep"? (98–99)

8. Even though he can't exchange the abbey for his loved ones and those who helped Robert during the war, why is old Faehmel "glad to have paid the price" with the destruction of the abbey, the work of his youth? (115)

9. Why is old Faehmel frightened of Schrella and his own son Robert? (92, 115, 163) Why does old Faehmel say that it wasn't until the war's persecution and violence reached an extreme that he abandoned his irony and "really understood and loved" his son and wife? (163)

10. When he sees the cake model of the abbey, why does old Faehmel move to smash it with his fist? Why does he instead cut off the spire and serve it to Robert? (280)

Suggested textual analyses

Pages 78–99 (from Chapter 4): beginning, "Later on, I often used to think back," and ending, "He nodded, smiled and left."

Pages 160–169 (from Chapter 6): from "When his father walked into the bar," to the end of the chapter.

Why does Robert adopt Hugo, "God's little lamb"?

1. Why do those who have tasted the *Host of the Beast* torment the "lambs" like Schrella and Hugo? Why does the author portray this as something that continues to occur after the war? (166)

2. Why does Hugo evoke cruelty in other children, while adults are attracted to him and want to exploit him? (18–19, 58–59)

3. Why does Robert think that once he asks Schrella why he is being tormented by Nettlinger and Old Wobbly "there would be no turning back"? Why does he think that this question is "burdened . . . with eternity"? (40–41)

4. Why is Robert described as neither a "lamb" nor a "beast," but as a "shepherd"? (42, 149, 159, 261)

5. Why does Robert tell Hugo stories about his life while he shoots billiards? Why is Hugo the only person other than Edith whom Robert tells about blowing up St. Anthony's Abbey? (62)

6. Why is it only in Hugo that Robert can see the smile of his wife Edith, and not in the faces of his and Edith's own children? (164, 268)

7. Why does Robert say to Schrella about Hugo, "Yes, we need him, and we'd be glad if he needed us. Better still—we're suffering from the want of him"? (268)

8. Why is it right that Hugo the lamb live with Robert, while Schrella the lamb does not? (268–269)

9. Why does the author have Robert go outside his family to adopt a new son, while Schrella is afraid even to have a child of his own? Why does Schrella say that he himself never married and had children because "that feeling in the blood is false, the other feeling alone is true"? (270)

10. Why, as he rescues Hugo from the shepherd-priestess, does Robert forget for the first time to say "please" when talking to him? (278)

Suggested textual analyses

Pages 58–64 (from Chapter 3): from "How about you, Hugo?" to the end of the chapter.

Pages 268–278 (from Chapter 13): beginning, " 'Yes,' Robert said, 'I still need him,' " and ending, "He could still hear her sobbing on his way down the service stairs."

FOR FURTHER REFLECTION

1. Was old Faehmel's dream of founding a dynasty of seven times seven grandchildren admirable or shallow?

2. Do you agree with Schrella that parents cannot tell of their children "of what host they'll partake"?

3. Do you think Robert found an effective way of dealing with social injustice in his wartime demolition? In his peacetime withdrawal from society?

4. Should not only vengeance but also forgiveness be left to God?

5. Is Böll too hard on the German people or not hard enough? How responsible are people for the outrages of their government?

6. Is there a "nobility of defenselessness," or must we always actively fight injustice?

7. Is the destruction of artistic or historical treasures a valid way to protest political injustice?

8. Was Johanna justified in her attempted murder of the former Nazi who was still active in German politics?

9. Has Böll effectively explained the causes of World War II without ever mentioning Hitler's name?

A C K N O W L E D G M E N T S

All possible care has been taken to trace ownership and secure permission for each selection in this anthology. The Great Books Foundation wishes to thank the following authors, publishers, and representatives for permission to reprint copyrighted material.

The Continuing Silence of a Poet, from THREE DAYS AND A CHILD, by A. B. Yehoshua. Translated by Miriam Arad. Copyright 1970 by the Institute for the Translation of Hebrew Literature, Ltd. Reprinted by permission of Doubleday, a division of Bantam Doubleday Dell Publishing Group, Inc.

Gwen and *Somewhere, Belgium,* from ANNIE JOHN, by Jamaica Kincaid. Copyright 1985 by Jamaica Kincaid. Reprinted by permission of Farrar, Straus & Giroux, Inc.

Iphigeneia at Aulis, by Euripides, from THE GREEK TRAGEDY IN NEW TRANSLATIONS, edited by William Arrowsmith. Translated by W. S. Merwin and George E. Dimock, Jr. Copyright 1978 by W. S. Merwin and George E. Dimock, Jr. Reprinted by permission of Oxford University Press, Inc.

Barn Burning, from COLLECTED STORIES OF WILLIAM FAULKNER, by William Faulkner. Copyright 1950 by Random House, Inc.; renewed 1977 by Jill Faulkner Summers. Reprinted by permission of Random House, Inc.

New African, from SARAH PHILLIPS, by Andrea Lee. Copyright 1984 by Andrea Lee. Reprinted by permission of Random House, Inc.